Creation Astronomy
A Study Guide to the
Constellations!

by
Felice Gerwitz and Jill Whitlock

Media Angels
Ft. Myers, Florida

Creation Science Study Guides™
© 1995 by Felice Gerwitz and Jill Whitlock
Revised 1997, 2003
ISBN# 1-931941-07-6
Published by Media Angels, Inc.
Ft. Myers, FL 33908
www.MediaAngels.com

Constellation star chart drawings by Jill Whitlock

Neither the publisher or authors shall be liable for any damage which may be caused as a result from conducting any of the experiments or activities in this book. Please note all cautions contained in this book.

Permission granted by Jim Kregel President of Kregel Publications to synopsize *Gospel in the Stars,* written by Joseph A. Seiss.

All scripture quotations are taken from The NIV Bible, Copyright 1983, Zondervan Bible Publishers.

This book is dedicated to the child in everyone who loves to lie on a blanket and look at the stars...

Psalm 19:1-3
"The heavens declare the glory of God; the skies proclaim the work of His hands.
Day after day they pour forth speech; night after night they display knowledge.
There is no speech or language where their voice is not heard."

Table of Contents

Introduction To Creation Astronomy

"The heavens declare the glory of God; the skies proclaim the work of His hands. Day after day they pour forth speech; night after night they display knowledge. There is no speech or language where their voice is not heard." (Psalm 19:1-3)

"And God said, Let there be lights in the firmament of the heavens to divide the day from the night; and *let them be for signs*, and for seasons, and for days, and years: And let them be for lights in the firmament of the heaven to give light upon the earth: and it was so. And God made two great lights; the greater light to rule the day, and the lesser light to rule the night: *He made the stars also.*" (King James Version Gen 1:14-16) (Author's emphais)

These were astonishing words for me when I read them after first becoming a Christian. When I first read the words, "The heavens declare the glory of God and show His handiwork," I thought that was pretty good because I have always enjoyed lying out in the grass and looking up at the stars. But I didn't understand how they could utter speech or show knowledge. God said that the lights were to be for *SIGNS*, and I wondered what signs and what they were for. And I thought that it was very interesting that all the stars in the universe were only given five words in Genesis "He made the stars also," and yet so much of what is taught about our universe and our world, and ingrained into our society as evolutionary thinking, has come from the study of the stars.

The universe and our solar system work with such regularity and predictability that it is impossible that they ever came about by chance. The relative position and motion of the sun, moon, and planets can be accurately predicted so that it is possible to send out a probe and have it visit the planets on a precise schedule years later. The motions of the stars are governed by the laws of physics. It is impossible that the orderliness and precision of the universe and the laws that govern it could have happened as the result of some accidental big explosion. All that can be expected from an explosion is chaos. Order must come from special design by a Designer.

A study of the original forty-eight constellations is used in this study of Creation Astronomy. Later or modern constellation names are not included. Most Christians avoid studying the stars because of the association with the wickedness of astrology, but God created those stars and He designed them to speak and show knowledge of Him; we need to get excited about the things that His Creation can teach us.

Just look at the constellations! There, right in front of us, is the Virgin, the Mother and Child, the serpent, the King, a Crown, the serpent going after the crown, the Great Physician grasping the serpent, the serpent striking a man's heel, the dying sacrifice, and the living fish which is the symbol of the Church. There is an altar, an arrow, a Cross, a stream of water symbolizing the Holy Spirit being poured out into the fish's mouth, and of course the Lion returning. Jesus was called 'The Lion of Judah."

On the Fourth Day of Creation, the Gospel message was written by the hand of God in the heavens long before He wrote His Gospel on paper. This precious message was given to us by Christ the Creator as He wrote out His plan for His own sacrifice from the very moment of Creation. We are given the gift of His inerrant Word written in the stars and in the Holy Bible — both written by the same Hand. The original salvation plan of God for His people was given to Adam in the Garden of Eden. I can just imagine God walking with Adam in the evenings, pointing out the constellations, and explaining everything to him. Then Adam was to pass that knowledge along to his sons and so forth.

There has been much excitement lately among astronomers, especially since the Hubble telescope had its vision repaired. Interestingly enough, the astronomers are having quite an argument among themselves about all the new data. Many have said that the astronomical community is in a state of confusion. A quote from the March 6, 1995, issue of *Time* magazine says that the new discoveries are turning the theories of the cosmos upside down. We are admonished from the Word of God to "turn away from godless chatter and the opposing ideas of what is falsely called knowledge, which some have professed and in doing so have wandered from the faith." (1 Timothy 6:20-21) All science is the study of God's Creation and unless that study is based on God's Word, it will be in error. The more I study Creation Science, the more I understand how great God really is. I hope that you will be as excited as I am about the study of the stars as God intended.

Jill Whitlock

Let's Do A Creation Astronomy Unit!

The study of the stars, or astronomy, is a very fascinating one. The exciting aspect of this unit is the story of the Gospel message in the stars. The original names of constellations, their meanings, and the Greek and Latin translations will be revealed. You will be amazed at the story as it unfolds showing the glory of God! You will easily spot the sections that Jill, the scientist, and Felice, the educator, have written! A special note: it was difficult to find Creation based astronomy books; therefore reading the Teaching Outline becomes of major importance. It will arm you with the facts from a Creationist's perspective to counteract the evolutionary claims found in many books.

Astronomy is the study of *space* and *the stars.* It is the study of *the sun, stars, constellations,* and *our galaxy.* In order for a scientific theory to be *valid,* it must be proven or disproven by testing or measuring. This is not possible with many of the theories or assumptions scientists have come up with to support claims about our universe. This book looks at science from a Creation standpoint. The stars were created in the distant past; scientists can at best only theorize as to their origin. Therefore, I consider faith to be an issue whether you believe in Creation or evolution. (For a study that features the origins of the earth, see *Creation Science: A Study Guide to Creation!)* In researching astronomy, you will find that various television shows, videos, books, articles, and computer programs almost exclusively deal with evolution.

This Astronomy study includes a *Teaching Outline.* It also includes an *outline for each grade level.* It is helpful to read the teaching outline to gain an insight into the material you will be presenting. We will explore the different *scientists,* and a *history of Astronomy,* along with the names of the original 48 *Constellations.* In order to get the most from this unit study, it is important to have a firm, basic understanding of Creation science, especially in the older grades, where an understanding of origins is desirable when comparing the two theories of origin (Creation and evolution).

To make this study useful to teachers of multi-aged children, it has been divided into three graded levels. The divisions are *K-3, 4-8,* and *9-12.* These are only guidelines. Feel free to pull information from any of the grade levels that you wish.

Another feature is *subject area* divisions following the study outlines to give you some ideas on how to incorporate *reading, vocabulary, spelling, grammar, language arts, math reinforcements, geography, history, science activities and experiments, art, and music.* I have noticed that many astronomy books duplicate each other in experiments and ideas. I have included the *ideas* I have found to be the most helpful. Many of the *games* and *activities* are original and have been played by the children in science workshops I have given and at home. Some are old favorites revised a little to fit the occasion! Most *books* listed in the resource section are readily available, and there is also a guide to *astronomy videos, cassettes, and computer programs.* I have included a *materials list* and *field trip guide.* I have also included pages you may copy containing the *scientific method* to assist you with your experiments.

An important point in this science unit study is a correct execution of the *scientific method.* The *scientific method* is a procedure used to do an experiment in an organized fashion. *The point of the scientific method is to solve a problem or further investigate an observation.* The steps of the scientific method are *asking a question, researching, forming an educated guess as to what the conclusion will be, doing the experiment, observing the results, and stating a conclusion.* Ideally the conclusion should be the answer to the original question, but alas, things being what they are, this is not always the case!

When teaching a new scientific concept, make sure you have your children tell you in their own words what they have just learned. For example, let's say you are teaching them about the speed of light. (It is important to remember to tie in experiments and activities to the topics you are learning.) You may want to do an experiment showing that light "appears" instantly; to do this you may turn a flashlight on to demonstrate your point. Be sure to ask questions such as, "Does light travel quickly? How do you know?" They should be able to tell you, "Yes, light travels quickly because when the flashlight was turned on the light was there instantly." This is a quick check to make sure they are following the concept and not getting side-tracked by the fun!

Science is always fun, but astronomy has been a favorite of mine for years. It is especially exciting and challenging to see how the stars were meant to tell about the Gospel! It's time to wait until evening, unroll a blanket, get out the binoculars, lie back and study God's Creation. Have fun learning about astronomy!

Felice Gerwitz

How to Prepare a Unit Study

What is a unit study?
  A unit study is taking one topic, in this case Creation astronomy, and interrelating all the other subjects into a unified teaching approach. In other words, while studying the topic of Creation astronomy, the children will *read* astronomy books and research materials, *write* assignments relating to what they've read, *spell* words they may have had difficulty reading or writing, *learn* vocabulary words dealing with astronomy, do *math problems* based on scientific principles, read and research *historical periods* relating to astronomy and time periods in which noteworthy evolutionists or Creation scientists lived, study *geographical locations* of scientific discoveries and Biblical events (i.e. what does the original Greek and Hebrew translation of the Constellations tell us?), create *art works* dealing with the constellations (such as drawing constellations depicting the original Greek and Hebrew definitions) and for m*usic* play instruments that make sounds similar to those in nature. In other words, all the subjects will relate to the main topic. (The authors suggest you supplement grammar, phonics and math with other programs, where age appropriate.)

Does a unit study cover all of the topics I need to teach in every grade?
  Yes and no! It depends on the grade level of your child and what your goals are for your home school. Many children know all they need to know for kindergarten by the time they are pre-schoolers. Thus, the kindergarten year is left free to implement unit studies on many different topics. Often, as the child progresses, because of all the reading research, projects and experimentation that he does, his learning will surpass what is generally considered "normal" for his grade level. Still, if you are concerned about standardized testing, the authors recommend you use these study guides as supplements to your core curriculum. However, in many cases, when homeschool students who have been taught with the unit study approach take a standardized test, they score in the 90+ percentile.

How do I begin planning?
  The best place to start is with a calendar, paper, pencil and the *Teaching Outline* in the study guide. We have provided lesson plans for you. Use these or the blank one provided and pencil in your own ideas. Write out a rough outline of the points you want to cover. You may use the ones provided in each of the three grade levels or you may utilize them as starters in creating your own outline. Reading the Teaching Outline will familiarize you with the topic. As you write your outline or points you want to cover, leave room for additions; i.e. you may run across a book or topic that you want to include. Decide how long you want to spend studying the topic. What months are you considering? Is this time before a major holiday? If so, you may want to do a shorter unit. Is it the beginning of school, summer, or other longer period of time? If so, you may wish to do a more complicated unit or spend more time digging deeper into the topic you choose. Decide what subjects you want to incorporate and what days you will do each. For example, you can spend every day reading, writing, doing grammar and math, but perhaps science experimentation and history will only be done three out of five days. You may prefer a Mon.-Wed.-Fri. / Tues.-Thurs. type of routine, or if you take Fridays off, your schedule might be Mon.- Wed. / Tues.-Thurs. (See scheduling on page seven.) Remember, it's up to you.

How do I begin using the Creation Study Guides?
  It doesn't take much time to plan, especially with our study guides. We've done much of the planning and research for you with an outline for each grade level and a *Teaching Outline* for referencing technical material. The grade level teaching outlines are geared for each of

three levels; K-3, 4-8 and 9-12. They are not as extensive as the Teaching Outline in the front of the book and younger grades will study less content than older students. The Teaching Outline is specifically geared for the parent, or older student, as preparation for understanding the topic. It will give you the necessary information and background necessary to teach the unit. We encourage you to read portions aloud to younger children and have older children read them alone or with you.

Plan to spend approximately six to eight weeks for this study. We have provided lesson plans which are sketched out for you with ideas for each week. You may take as long as you wish. (We feel this is an excellent preparation to counter secular materials where it is almost impossible to avoid the evolutionary viewpoint.)

If you have older and younger children, try to find a middle ground as a starting place. Look through the activities and suggested assignments. Check off the ones that interest you in each subject area and pencil into the provide lesson plans. Decide which supplemental books you will need and plan on obtaining them. Interlibrary loans are able to obtain books from private as well as public libraries. We don't suggest you use every book we recommend. We usually list a greater number of books than necessary so that if you can't obtain one particular book you may be able to find another. Use topic related books when you can not obtain the ones we recommend.

How do I test to find out if my children have learned what I am teaching with the unit approach?

We have found that working closely with our children tells us all we need to know about what they know and don't know. By reading materials orally and then verbally questioning them, we know what needs review and what doesn't. They do many hands on activities that reinforce previously read materials. For example, in *Creation Science: A Study Guide to Creation!* there is a discussion on evolutionary principles. One of the points made is how evolution violates the second law of thermodynamics. That in itself sounds very dry and scholarly, yet a follow-up activity presented after the discussion is the "Entropy" experiment which is a very visual way to reinforce what they have learned. If the children can explain it to you, then you know they understand the concept. After reading all this, if you feel the need to create tests to find out what they know, feel free to do so! You could easily generate oral tests for the little ones, and essay questions for the older ones. One of the great things about homeschooling is the freedom to teach as you wish.

What about co-oping?

Co-oping is teaching a unit study with another family (or several families) and taking time once a week, or more, to work together on projects, experiments or activities for the entire day. Each family focuses on the unit materials at home during the week, and the co-op is a way of reinforcing the subjects taught at home. This unit lends itself well to co-ops. There are many experiments that would be fun to do as a group. Still, they can be done just as easily with a single family. The choice is up to you.

Try not to get bogged down and become a slave to a schedule (recipe for disaster!). While Jill was living in Washington state, a friend of hers was doing a unit on Washington state history. They traveled all over the state visiting historical sites. After a boat ride to see the Orcas migrating, they were so intrigued, they visited the Sea-aquarium and beaches, etc. Soon they realized they were no longer doing a unit on history but one on marine biology. That's they way unit studies should flow. Get ready to have a great time, and better yet, teach in a way that makes great memories that are remembered year after year after year...

Scheduling and Planning

For those of you who would like help planning a schedule for this study, I have drawn up some thumbnail sketches below to use as a basis for planning. Please use these loosely and feel free to add or delete anything you wish. Notice I have not included times. This is intentional, as there is no way I can know what will work for you and your family. The next page contains a blank weekly lesson plan sheet. Before each grade level you will find weekly lesson plans if you wish for a more planned chart.

Schedule A:

Monday	Tuesday	Wednesday	Thursday	Friday
Bible/Prayer	Bible/Prayer	Bible/Prayer	Bible/Prayer	Bible/Prayer
Suggested reading	Language Arts activities	Suggested reading	Language Arts activities	Suggested reading
Vocabulary/ Spelling and Grammar	Math reinforcements	Vocabulary/ Spelling and Grammar	Math reinforcements	Vocabulary/ Spelling and Grammar
Science activities	Geography/History	Science activities	Geography/History	Science activities
Art	Music	Art	Music	Art

Schedule B:

Monday	Tuesday	Wednesday	Thursday	Friday
Bible/Prayer	Bible/Prayer	Bible/Prayer	Bible/Prayer	Bible/Prayer
Suggested reading	Math reinforcements	Suggested reading	Math reinforcements	Suggested reading
Language Arts activities	Vocabulary/ Spelling and Grammar	Language Arts activities	Vocabulary/ Spelling and Grammar	Language Arts activities
Geography/History	Science activities	Geography/History	Science activities	Geography/History
Finish activities	Music	Finish activities	Art	Finish activities

Schedule C:

Monday	Tuesday	Wednesday	Thursday	Friday
Bible/Prayer	Bible/Prayer	Bible/Prayer	Bible/Prayer	Bible/Prayer
Math textbook	Math textbook	Math textbook	Math textbook	Math textbook
Reading/Phonics program	Reading/Phonics program	Reading/Phonics program	Reading/Phonics program	Reading/Phonics program
Suggested reading	Math reinforcements	Suggested reading	Math reinforcements	Suggested reading
Language Arts activities	Vocabulary/ Spelling and Grammar	Language Arts activities	Vocabulary/ Spelling and Grammar	Language Arts activities
Science activities	Geography/History	Science activities	Geography/History	Science activities
Music	Art	Music	Art	Music

Lesson Plans

Subject	Monday	Tuesday	Wednesday	Thursday	Friday
Bible/Religion Studies					
Astronomy Teaching Outline					
Reading Selection					
Vocab/Spell/ Grammar Language Arts					
Math Reinforcement					
Science Activities and Experiments					
Geography/History Ideas					
Art/Music					

LA= Language Arts   CR= Creation Resource
TS= Teacher Selection

Teaching Outline

I. THE SCIENTIFIC STUDY OF ASTRONOMY

The Ancient Astronomers — The Oldest Scientists
Astronomy is the oldest science with a history of thousands of years. Ancient astronomers were drawing phases of the moon thousands of years ago. Caves in Spain have been found that contain paintings of the changes in the phases of the moon. In various parts of Europe, stones have been set up as astronomical observatories, the most famous being the one at Stonehenge. The arches of these stone observatories mark the rising and setting of the sun and the moon and determine the seasons by the movement through these arches. Long before the invention of the telescope, astronomers were diligently studying the night skies. The earliest records are on some 3000-year-old Babylonian clay tablets used to record the movements of the sun, moon and planets. Some of these clay tablets were precise astronomical tables used to accurately determine the eclipses of the sun and moon.

The Greeks — The ancient Greeks thought that the earth was flat. Around 500 B.C. a mathematician named Pythagoras had a theory that the earth was a sphere and the stars were in a sphere around the earth. He also thought that the earth traveled around a central fire once a day. Aristotle and Ptolemy both thought that the earth was at the center of the universe and that everything else revolved around it.

Nicolaus Copernicus (1473-1543) — Copernicus was a Polish astronomer who was the first to explain that the planets moved around the sun in circular orbits. He is known as the Father of Modern Astronomy. His discoveries were all made without the aid of a telescope! Copernicus published his findings May 24, 1543.

Tycho Brahe (1546-1601) — Brahe was a Danish astronomer who worked under the King of Denmark and was able to make detailed records of the movements of the stars and planets. Even though he believed that the earth was at the center of the universe, he was able to provide tables of planetary motion and the position of 777 fixed stars. He hired Johannes Kepler as his assistant a year before he died. (The New Book Of Knowledge, s.v. "Astronomy")

Johannes Kepler (1571-1630) — Kepler benefited from working under Tycho Brahe and he improved Copernicus's idea of planetary motion. He discovered that the planets orbited the sun in elliptical orbits rather than circular ones, and he came up with the Laws of Planetary Motion. Being a Christian and a mathematician, Kepler believed that God used mathematics to design the universe with its orderliness and precision.

Galileo Galilei (1564-1642) — When Galileo heard of the invention of the telescope, then called a spyglass, he wanted one to help him with his study of astronomy, so he built one. With his telescope he discovered that Jupiter had moons and that Venus went through phases and therefore had to revolve around the sun. He noticed spots on the sun that appeared to move from day to day, and that led him to the conclusion that the sun was turning on its axis.

Isaac Newton (1642-1727) —   An English scientist, mathematician and astronomer, Newton invented the first reflecting telescope. Through mathematics, Kepler came up with the law of universal gravitation to explain the orbits of the planets around the sun. He also proved mathematically that Kepler's laws of planetary motion were correct. (*The New Book Of Knowledge*, s.v. "Astronomy")

Modern Observers —   Astronomers set up a brightness scale to assign stars a relative brightness called apparent magnitude. This scale is called the Pogson Scale where lower numbers indicate brighter stars and higher numbers indicate fainter stars. Our sun has a magnitude of 4.8 on this scale,and Sirius, one of our brightest stars, has a magnitude of -1.46. In order to calculate the absolute magnitude of the stars we would have to know the distance to them. *(Bliss 1991)*

Big Bang Theory — Modern Astronomers
The Big Bang Theory came about because man, in his sinful nature, had to find a way to explain the marvels and complexities of the universe without any Divine intervention. To admit the abrupt appearance of the universe, created out of nothing, by Special Design, would be the same as admitting that there was a God. Not wanting to believe there is a Creator, man came up with an explanation of the origin of the entire universe through natural physical laws. The problem with that is that the laws cannot always explain everything and one is left with the question of where the original matter came from, and how and why it exploded.

An Explanation — This theory of the origin of the universe states that all the matter in the universe was once condensed into an infinitely small dot that contained an infinite amount of mass and energy. This dot exploded (no explanation for the explosion is ever given) and the explosion formed all the chemical elements. By some unknown process, protons and neutrons were able to come together to form nuclei, and then by some other unknown process, these new nuclei were able to combine with the appropriate number of electrons. This explosion threw matter out into space for millions and billions of years. At some point, gravity became an effective force (no explanation is given for why particles of matter would start to attract together rather than continue to expand out into space) and matter began to clump into primordial swirling gases. These clouds of swirling gases formed the first protogalaxies which were cold and dark and without stars. From these *cold* protogalaxies came the galaxies: clusters of stars which are *very hot,* burning stellar objects. It is of interest to note that not all scientists agree with the Big Bang Theory, and many have never agreed with it at all.

Some History —   In the 1920s, Edwin Hubble discovered that distant stars apparently had their light waves lengthened or shifted toward the red end of the spectrum.

This is what we now call the red-shift. Hubble interpreted this red-shift to mean that the stars were moving away from earth, and this moving away was responsible for lengthening of the light waves. Therefore, he concluded that the universe was expanding. He established a value known as the Hubble constant (which has never been agreed upon by astronomers and has never been constant). This constant is the ratio of how fast the galaxies are flying apart and how far away they are from earth. It is expressed in terms of kilometers per second per megaparsec of distance. David Branch, an astrophysicist from the University of Oklahoma says that there are these two loopholes in the constant; "...what's the right distance and what's the right speed." (Lemonick 1995)

Since 1921 the Lithium content of many old stars has been found to contradict the predictions of the Big Bang Theory. As one of the light elements, being number three on the periodic table, it should be present in greater abundance.

In 1931, Abbe' Lamaitre put forth a theory that the universe originated as a single particle of vast energy and near-zero radius called the 'primeval atom'. No explanation was given as to where the energy came from.

In the 1940s Hubble caused quite a stir when he announced that the universe was only two billion years old. Geologists, of course, believed that the earth itself was over twice that old.

In 1946 scientists working on the Manhattan Project postulated that a universal explosion lasting a few seconds could have produced all the elements we see today. This lost favor with other scientists, however, a decade later, when it could not explain how light elements could come together to form the heavy elements.

In 1948 Sir Fred Hoyle and a group of others were studying how to account for the excess of hydrogen in the universe. They came up with the 'steady-state theory' which suggests that matter first appeared in masses of hydrogen gas that exist in space where there are few stars, and that new matter is being created continuously. This is contrary to the First Law of Thermodynamics which states that energy, which is related to matter, cannot be created or destroyed.

In 1965 Robert Dicke and others discovered that the universe had a background temperature of three degrees Kelvin (that is three degrees above absolute zero). This was interpreted as the after glow of an initial explosion. There was no explanation as to why it would be a consistent temperature and not warmer toward the point of the supposed initial explosion.

In 1965 Sir Fred Hoyle did some mathematical calculations that 'proved' that a Big Bang would produce only light elements. This was widely accepted as the 'proof' of the Big Bang Theory. This was later proven false.

In the 1970s Astronomer William G. Tiff showed that red-shifts tend to occur at regular intervals and are evenly dispersed, like the rungs of a ladder, not smoothed out and even as would be expected if the universe were expanding. No one has ever seen the universe expanding; it is merely assumed as an interpretation of the red-shift. Many astronomers and physicists are beginning to wonder what the red-shifts really mean.

In the 1980s astronomical calculations showed that the detected matter in the universe is only 1% of the amount required to produce the gravitational attraction needed to form all the galaxies and clusters of galaxies, (even given vast amounts of time such as the hypothetical twenty billion years). In other words, 99% of the universe is missing. So astrophysicists have solved this enigma by deciding that 99% of the universe is made up of "Cold Dark Matter" (CDM). Although it can't be seen, or detected, astronomers say it has to be there or the universe wouldn't hold together. (Lemonick 1995) This contradicts Hebrews 1:3 which states that God holds all things together by His powerful word. What is observed in the universe is galaxies in clusters, rather than evenly dispersed. This is what would be expected by a Creationist who believes the Genesis account of Creation.

In 1991 Eric Lerner came up with the 'plasma theory' to try to account for the excess hydrogen in the universe because plasma has movement and electrical currents in it. Our own Aurora Borealis and Aurora Australis (the Northern Lights and the Southern Lights) are examples of plasma energy. Plasma is clouds of electrically charged subatomic particles and is sometimes called the fourth state of matter. (The first state of matter is physical: what we know as know as solid, liquid and gas. For example, gold ore is in the physical state. It can be made into gold coins, but physically it is still gold. The second state of matter involves a chemical change such as occurs when a piece of wood is burned. Energy is released as the wood burns, and a chemical change takes place in the wood. The third state of matter involves a change in the nucleus of an atom. This change in the nucleus of an atom is called fission or splitting of the atom, and tremendous amounts of energy are released in the process.) As atoms leave the sun traveling at the speed of light, this extreme speed strips the electron shells from the atoms, leaving the nuclei as a charged particle. When these charged particles enter the earth's magnetic field, they interact with it in the ionosphere and the result is the beautiful light display seen in the northern and southern latitudes. (*The New Book Of Knowledge,* s.v. "Energy")

In 1993, astrophysicist George Efstathiou stated, "In my view, cosmologists should not be too disturbed about discrepancies between theory and observation. It is not surprising that things don't fit...the history of the evolutionary theory from the time of Darwin to the present has been a <u>conflict between theory and facts</u>." (Lemonick 1995)

In 1993 F. Wagner Schlessinger wrote in the *Compton's Interactive Encyclopedia* under the topic of Relativity, "Stellar Shift Verified — Another consequence of the Theory [of Relativity] is a shift of spectral lines toward the RED, caused by the huge masses in stars 'dragging back' or slowing down upon their own light. This effect is hard to distinguish from the so-called 'red-shift' which suggests that the universe may be expanding." "Red-Shift" refers to the lengthening of light waves and is similar to the Doppler effect on sound. In the visible light spectrum, the red light waves are the longest and the blue light waves are the shortest. If a light wave were lengthened, it would then be shifted toward the red end of the spectrum. Conversely, if a light wave were compressed or shortened, its wave length would be shifted toward the blue end of the spectrum of visible light. This is analogous to standing on a street corner as an ambulance goes by. As the ambulance approaches your position, the sound waves are compressed and the sound appears to be higher. When the ambulance passes your position and is moving away from you, the sound waves are lengthened and the sound appears to be lower. However, if you were riding inside the ambulance, the pitch of the sound would apparently be constant. But as we have just learned from Mr. F. Wagner Schlessinger, there is another possible and probable explanation for the lengthening of the light waves emitted from stars.

Some Problems For the Big Bang Theory

Galaxy Clusters — Astronomers are perplexed by the clusters of galaxies in the universe. Nowhere are there any single field galaxies seen. All the galaxies should have dispersed because they have been in motion during the twenty billion years since the universe was formed by the Big Bang, if the universe were actually old and receding. This presents another enigma for astronomers. If the universe is only about 6000 years old as told in the Creation account in Genesis, then one would expect to see the galaxies still clumped together in clusters which is what we observe.

Spiral Arms — When observing galaxies, it is noticed that they have two to three arms spiraling out from the central mass. If these galaxies had been rotating for very long, there should be hundreds of arms coming out of them by now. Because only two to three arms are observed, this is a good indication that they are very young. There is a feature out there in space known as a barred spiral galaxy. This is a galaxy where part of each arm coming out of the central core is straight; it has not yet been forced into a spiral by the rotation of the galaxy. Astronomers have determined the rotational velocity of one such barred spiral galaxy. It takes approximately 100 million years for this galaxy to make one complete rotation. Because these arms are still partly straight (barred), this indicates that this galaxy has only made one-eighth of a rotation. Therefore, it has only been around 12.5 million years (one-eighth of one hundred million is 12.5 million). Clearly this is much younger than astronomers would like to admit. And there are numerous barred spiral galaxies.

Comets — As comets pass by our sun, the power emitted from the sun blows away parts of the comet partially disintegrating them. The visible tail of the comet is that part that is being blown away. Therefore, the comets will eventually disintegrate completely. The measured rate of comet disintegration has forced scientists to realize that all short-term comets would be gone in 10,000 years. We have five million comets still orbiting our solar system, which is a great indication that the universe is young. But because this presents another enigma to astronomers, a gentleman named Jan Oort has postulated an imaginary "nest of comets" out there somewhere. No one has ever seen this nest of comets, now called the Oort Cloud, but astronomers say it must be there, and periodically it shakes loose some new comets that then enter our solar system, and that, according to the astronomers, explains why there are five million comets still orbiting our system.

Accretion Disks and The Law of the Conservation of Angular Momentum — Our solar system, according to the Big Bang, began by forming an accretion disk of gas and ice-coated pebbles. There is no explanation as to how the ice formed (there first had to be water) or where the pebbles came from, but all of a sudden there were materials swirling around together. The ice-coated pebbles gathered into swarms and then formed boulders, and gravitational attractions took over. Note that all this matter would now be swirling in the same direction. The Law of the Conservation of Angular

Momentum states that for any spinning object, when pieces fly off the spinning object, they will continue to spin in the same direction as the main body. For example, if several blocks were placed on a merry-go-round and it was then speeded up to the point where the blocks began to fly off the merry-go-round, the blocks would spin in the same direction as the merry-go-round. Therefore, if our solar system formed from an accretion disk, then all the bodies within it should be spinning in the same direction. The planets orbit counter-clockwise around the sun. The sun itself, however, spins clockwise. This does not support the Big Bang. Venus and Neptune spin backwards as they move counter-clockwise around the sun. Uranus lies on its side. There are sixty moons in our solar system. Of those, eleven spin backwards and four even travel backwards. Two planets have moons traveling in both directions. If our solar system formed from an accretion disk, then all these bodies should be traveling in the same direction. This is another enigma that cannot be explained by the Big Bang Theory.

Lumpy Rings — Voyager 2 sent many wonderful pictures of our solar system back to earth. Pictures of Neptune astonished astronomers with images of the lumpy rings around it. Lumpy rings indicate youth, because if they had been there for very long, they would have smoothed out long before now. Saturn's ring system also shows interesting features and lumpiness. If Saturn were 4.5 billion years old, then the rings should be in very stable condition. If astronomers accepted the fact that Saturn, Earth and the universe are only about 6000 years old, then there would be no enigma. The reason that lumpy rings are surprising in a universe that is assumed to be very old is because of the Poynting-Robertson Effect. This is the effect that the sun's gravity has on all objects orbiting it. The sun's gravity slightly slows down the object (which can be anything from a microscopic piece of space dust to boulders in the rings of Saturn.) This effect is likened to rain drops hitting the windshield of a small car as it goes down the highway. If you could precisely measure it, you could determine that the raindrops hitting the windshield were slowing the forward progress of the vehicle. This effect would be much less on a very large semi-tractor trailer moving on the same highway. The raindrops would have less effect on the trailer. (Akerman 1993) What this means is that over a long period of time, the particles in space will reach a state of gradation from fine to very coarse. The drag effect on particles in space is explained mathematically by the Poynting-Robertson Effect and the equations of motion and the effects of solar radiation and re-radiation by the particles and the gravitational con-sideration. A detailed explanation is in the book, *The Age of the Solar System; A Study of the Poynting-Robertson Effect and Extinction of Interplanetary Dust* by Harold S. Slusher and Stephen Robertson, published by the Institute for Creation Research.

Warm Planets — The earth is losing its heat. Even though we are warmed daily by our star, there is still a net heat loss of 10 to the 27th power calories per second per day. If the earth were 4.5 billion years old, it should be stone cold to the very core due to entropy alone. Jupiter is also a very warm planet that should have gone cold given vast eons of time. Our own moon, which has no atmosphere, still has some measurable warmth at its core. The fact that these planetary bodies in our solar system still have warmth is an enigma for evolutionary thinking and a very good indicator that the solar system is very young.

Venus — The Magellan spacecraft has revealed fascinating pictures of the surface of Venus. The photos portray a surprisingly young-looking landscape. Evolutionary thinking would say that Venus is billions of years old, but these pictures reveal only 800 to 900 impact craters with sharp peaks, which indicate that it is very young. The Magellan scientists came up with a theory that somehow the surface of Venus was recycled and wiped clean by a planet-wide catastrophe in order to explain the apparent young age of Venus. (Wieland 1994)

The Sun — The source of the sun's energy is still being debated. A program on PBS showed how scientists were trying to prove that thermo-nuclear fusion was the sun's energy source. They were trying to capture neutrinos (a by-product of nuclear fission) inside an abandoned gold mine where these scientists have built huge pieces of equipment and sensitive monitoring devices used to capture and count neutrinos. Over the last ten years and with millions of taxpayer dollars, they have captured only six neutrinos. This does not prove that the source of the sun's energy is thermo-nuclear. However, 150 years ago it was postulated that gravitational collapse was the source of the sun's energy. Measurements of the sun's diameter over the last 300 years indicate that the sun is shrinking at the rate of five feet per hour. This gives a shrinkage rate of 1% every 1000 years. Going back twenty million years would place the sun's diameter out to where the earth is now. No dinosaurs could have lived here seventy five million years ago, for the earth would have been inside the sun. Even 100,000 years ago life on earth would have been impossible. If, however, the earth and the sun are only 6000 years old, then the sun would be only 6% larger than it is now, and the temperature on earth would have been only slightly warmer than it is now, which fits into the Creation model of a young universe.(Petersen 2002). Most people think that our sun is a rather small, ordinary star. The truth, however, is that the sun is not ordinary. Most stars are variable stars, which means that their brightness fluctuates from very dim to very bright. If our star were not shining at a constant rate, life on earth would not be possible. No life could tolerate the extremes in temperature caused by a variable star. Another important factor that makes our star so extraordinary is that astronomers have never found another star with a system of planets orbiting it. They see what they describe a perturbations in the supposed motion of a distant star and have interpreted this to be evidence of the presence of planets or-biting this star. The ratio of the earth to the sun is very similar to that of a pea to a basketball. If you were to place a pea in your front yard and the basketball in your backyard 126 feet apart, this would give you a good idea of the relationship of the earth to the sun.

The Moon — Astronomers have measured that the moon is moving away from the earth at the rate of two inches per year. This means that two billion years ago it would have been touching the earth. If it started out away from the earth, it would be out of sight in 4.5 billion years. (Petersen 1990)

The Trapezium of Orion — There are four stars inside the constellation of Orion that form a group called the Trapezium. Astronomers have given each of these very different ages. But, they have also found that these four stars are moving away from each other at extremely fast speeds. If the course and speed of these four stars were plotted backward, they would come to a common point of origin just 10,000 years ago. The ages assigned to these stars by astronomers are much older than that, and thus present another enigma to the scientists. If these stars came from a common point just 10,000 years ago, how can the stars themselves be older than that?

Time Magazine Article -- The cover story for the March 6th, 1995 *Time* magazine was "When Did the Universe Begin?" The new information astronomers have been analyzing since the Hubble telescope had its vision repaired, has left them in a state of chaos and constantly arguing with each other over the age of the universe. One analysis says that the universe is not expanding but rather is moving toward Virgo. Other astronomers want to throw this information out because it doesn't fit with their cosmological theories; even though they cannot prove the analysis to be incorrect, they insist that it must be incorrect.

According to the article, many astronomers are angry at their fellow scientists who say that the universe is now only eight billion years old, as they hold tenaciously to the twenty-billion-year old age of the universe. There is a great gulf between theory and observation as each scientist plugs his 'pet theory' into a computer with his 'pet parameters' and has his or her desired results printed out. If the universe is only eight billion years old, then what is to be done about the stars that have been assigned ages much older than the universe itself? The following is a quote from page 78 of the *Time* magazine article:

"In fairness, it must be acknowledged that cosmologists have had very little information to go on, at least until very recently. The distant galaxies that bear witness to the universe's origin, evolution and structure are excruciatingly faint, and it takes every bit of skill observers have to tease out their secrets. In a very real sense, cosmology has only lately crossed the dividing line from theology into true science. ....The experts don't know for sure how old or how big the universe is. They don't know what most of it is made of. They don't know in any detail how it began or how it will end. And, beyond the local cosmic neighborhood, they don't know much about what it looks like." In other words, they don't know much about anything in the universe, yet they are professing theories of its origin to the public as though they are facts. In actuality, the newly acquired data doesn't match their own hypothesis and astronomers have no explanations.

Reversal Of Opinion – A revealing article in the magazine "Infinite Energy" entitled, *The Implications of the "Big Bang"*, written by Dr. Eugene F. Mallove shows an amazing reversal of opinion. Dr. Mallove wrote a book in 1987 entitled, *The Quickening Universe*: *Cosmic Evolution and Human Destiny* that was a defense of the Big Bang theory. In this article, published in December of 2002, Dr. Mallove writes, "This, my first book, was based on the collected wisdom of the cosmologists and biologists whom I had studied and believed. I now reject that tidy picture, which rested on what I *then* thought was a sound theoretical framework underlying the basic" Big Bang" cosmology, one based on multiple interlocking streams of experimental evidence."
(Mallove 2002) He further writes, "I have come to realize that there are many reasons to reject the Big Bang, almost all having to do with the manner in which the physics

community misrepresents fundamental data, which it claims supports the Big Bang." (Mallove 2002) Here is a secular scientist, who certainly is not embracing the Creation Model of how the Universe began, but with enough scientific integrity to reject the much flawed Big Bang theory. While enumerating the many reasons to reject the Big Bang theory, Dr. Mallove states, "We need not review all the reasons to reject the Big Bang...beyond mentioning that many early twentieth century and present explanations for the cosmic background radiation exist that have nothing to do with a Big Bang, that photographic and radio telescope evidence exists to challenge the very basis of the expanding universe (the interpretation of galactic red shift as cosmic expansion), or that cosmic light element distribution data have literally been *fudged* into agreeing with an early hot universe Big Bang theory. That's enough!" (Mallove 2002) He realizes that most of the scientific community does not view their data with an unbiased interpretation, but rather tries to skew and, in his words, fudge the data to come out with their preconceived conclusions.

Dr. Tom Van Flandern received a PhD. in astronomy from Yale and had a twenty year career with the Navy at the US Naval Observatory, wrote the article, "The Top 30 Problems with the Big Bang." In the abstract of this paper, Dr Van Flandern writes, "Perhaps never in the history of science has so much quality evidence accumulated against a model so widely accepted within a field. Even the most basic elements of the theory—the expansions of the universe and the fireball remnant radiation — remain interpretations with credible alternative explanations." (Van Flandern 2002)

I will synopsize some of the problems listed. "1. Static universe models fit observable data better than expanding universe models." The major tenant of the Big Bang theory is that the universe began from an explosion at one point and continues to expand out from that point. The data however, tend to support the steady state or static model. "Static universe models match most observations with NO adjustable parameters. The Big Bang can match each of the critical observations, but ONLY with adjustable parameters, one of which (the cosmic deceleration parameter) requires mutually exclusive values to match different tests. Without ad hoc theorizing, this point alone falsifies the Big Bang." This is a very dramatic statement by a cosmic scientist refuting the Big Bang.

"2. The microwave 'background' makes more sense as the limiting temperature of space heated by starlight than as the remnant of a fireball." (Van Flandern 2002) Most scientists believe that the temperature in space was left over from the heat of the initial explosion (Big Bang). But what is observed is a uniform background of 2.8 degrees Kelvin as a natural minimum temperature due to all the stars heating up space. If this temperature was from an initial explosion at one point in space, then we should see a gradation in temperature outward from that spot. The brightness ratio of radio galaxies at infrared and radio wavelengths changes with distance in a way which implies absorption. Basically, this means that the longer wavelengths are more easily absorbed by material between the galaxies. But then the microwave radiation (between the two wavelengths) should be absorbed by the medium too, and has no chance to reach us from such great distances, or to remain perfectly uniform while doing so. It must instead result from the radiation of microwaves from the intergalactic medium. This argument alone implies that the microwaves could not be coming directly to us from a distance beyond all the galaxies, and therefore that the Big Bang theory cannot be correct. Clearly, without a realistic quantitative prediction, the Big Bang's hypothetical "fireball" becomes indistinguishable from the natural minimum temperature of all cold matter in space." (Van Flandern 2002)

"3. Element abundance predictions using the Big Bang require too many adjustable parameters to make them work." (Van Flandern 2002) Fred Hoyle correctly predicted the abundance of elements heavier than lithium. When the proponents of the Big Bang used the same parameters they did not work unless these parameters were adjusted, tweaked, and otherwise fudged for each element.

"4. The universe has too much large scale structure (interspersed "walls" and voids) to form in a time as short as 10-20 billion years." (Van Flandern 2002) It has been observed in space that there are massive areas of build up of galaxies called walls and even more massive areas between them where no galaxies exist called voids. Secular astronomers believe that it would be over 100 billion years, considering the speed of the galaxies, for these phenomenon to occur. However, a Creation scientist looks at this and sees a very young universe of only a few thousand years that has not had enough time to even out over space.

"5. The average luminosity of quasars must decrease with time in just the right way so that their average apparent brightness is the same at all red-shifts, which is exceedingly unlikely." (Van Flandern 2002) Again this requires significant adjustments of the parameters in order to fit the observable universe.

"6. The age of globular clusters appear older then the universe." (Van Flandern 2002) This is a major problem for astronomers because you can't be older than your mom.

"7. The local streaming motions of galaxies are too high for a finite universe that is supposed to be everywhere uniform." (Van Flandern 2002) What this means is that there are redshifts that the Big Bang cannot explain and differences across opposite sides of the galaxy that the scientists call puzzling. The only possible way to explain them would be to assume that the back ground microwave radiation is in motion relative to us here on Earth. Both of these scenarios mean Big Trouble for the Big Bang.

"8. Invisible dark matter of an unknown but non-baryonic nature must be the dominant ingredient of the entire universe." Van Flandern 2002) According to the Big Bang theory there is not enough matter in the universe for it to hold together and behave as it does. Therefore scientists came up with this invisible, undetectable matter to answer the gravitational questions. This is just one more gigantic fudge factor that this theory needs. However, a scientist named Milgrom came up with a model for the universe that does not require modifying the Law of Gravity and also eliminates the need for the existence of invisible dark matter.

"9. The most distant galaxies in the Hubble Deep Field show insufficient evidence of evolution, with some of them having higher redshifts ($z=6-7$) than the highest redshift quasars." (Van Flandern 2002) According to the Big Bang theory galaxies and stars in the "early universe" must be primitive meaning that they should be free of metal. However the latest evidence indicates there is lots of metal in the so-called earliest galaxies. Another 'oops' for the Big Bang.

The following quote from Dr. Ton Van Flandern should be required reading for all astronomers, remember that he is a secular scientist:

"Anyone doubting the Big Bang in its present form (which includes most astronomy-interested people outside the field of astronomy, according to one recent survey) would have good cause for that opinion and could easily defend such a position. This is a fundamentally different matter than proving the Big Bang did not happen, which would be proving a negative—something that is normally impossible (e.g., we cannot prove that Santa Claus does not exist). The Big Bang, much like the Santa Claus hypothesis, no longer makes testable predictions wherein proponents agree that a failure would falsify the hypothesis. Instead, the theory is continually amended to account for all new, unexpected discoveries.

There are many more problems for the Big Bang theory and I encourage you to research them and see for yourself. I think the problems with the Big Bang theory can be summed up nicely with this quote from Arnold G. Gulko, "When we look for predictions of the Big Bang theory which have been correct, or observations which have been logically explained, it is hard to find them. All we find is a compilation of wild and unsupported possibilities." (Gulko 2002)

The Speed of Light —
Speed of Light Today — The speed of light today is 186,262 miles per second or 299,792,000 meters per sec. Because light takes time to travel, evolutionary scientists believe that the light we now receive from distant stars and galaxies left there millions and billions of years ago. Thus they appear, to us here on earth, as they were millions or billions of years ago. These scientists believe that the deeper they look into space, the farther back they see in time. Therefore if they calculate a star to be 100 million light-years away, it must be at least 100 million years old, and the light we see here on earth shows us what the stars looked like as if it was 100 million years ago. If the astronomers calculate a star to be fifteen billion light-years away, then it must be at least fifteen billion years old and we are seeing it here on earth as it was fifteen billion years ago. These scientists admit that they can see only so far back and that initial stages, including the big bang itself, lie beyond detection. Astronomers also admit that their determination of distances past 50,000 light-years really falls apart and is actually only guesswork. (Lemonick 1995). The latest problem asronomers have with the "new" age of the universe, allocated from the new data from the Hubble telescope, is that there are stars in the universe that "appear" to be older than the universe itself. How can this be, since, as one astronomer put it, "You can't be older than your ma!" Astronomers have recently reported finding what they call stellar nurseries where they believe stars are being "born." What they see are bright spots that they *assume* are new stars. Astronomers have calculated a very complex series of theoretical events that they "believe" occur in the lifecycle of a star and that supposedly take *millions of years.* However, an article published in 1991 points out that a certain star, FG Sagittae, was observed to change from a blue star at 12,000 degrees Kelvin to a yellow star with 500 degrees Kelvin in only *thirty-six years*. This observation breaks down the astronomers' stellar series of long ages of time in the lifecycle of stars. (Wieland 1996)

Speed of Light and the Six Days of Creation — When the sun, moon, and stars were created on the fourth day, their light reached the earth instantaneously. In Genesis 1:14-15 God says that the lights in the sky are created first "for signs" and then "to mark the seasons and days and years...and to give light to the earth."

15

Creationists believe there was no waiting around for years for the light from the nearest star to reach Earth. Much of the vast amount of time associated with the age of the universe and evolution comes from the interpretation of modern astronomers.

According to Einstein's general theory of relativity, gravity affects time. This gravitational time dilation has been confirmed by observation and shows that clocks located at sea level or low altitudes tick slower than clocks at high altitudes. In his book, *Starlight and Time: Solving the Puzzle of Distant Starlight in a Young Universe*, Russell Humphryes explains that while six regular days were passing here on earth during the Creation Week, the gravitational time dilation would have allowed for much longer periods of time to pass at the most distant stars. The following explanation is a quote from Dr. Humphryes' book: "The mathematics of this new theory shows that while God makes the universe in six days *in the earth's reference frame* (Earth Standard Time, if you like), the light had ample time *in the extra-terrestrial reference frame* to travel the required distances. None of these time frames can be said to be "God's time" since the Creator, who sees the end from the beginning (Isaiah 46:10, Rev. 22:13, John 8:58 and more) is outside of time. Time is a created feature of His universe, like matter and space. It is interesting that the equations of GR (general relativity) have long indicated that time itself had a beginning." (*Humphreys 1995*)

An analogy for this theory of light traveling from distant stars is that they move much like a line of marchers in a band as they turn a corner. The person on the inside of the corner (Earth) takes tiny steps and covers a very short distance. In the same amount of time, the marcher on the farthest end of the line (distant stars) must take very large steps and cover a much greater distance in the same amount of time. If you used the same increments to measure the time and distance traveled by the marcher on the inside of the corner, then the marcher farthest away would look as if he had been traveling a very long time.

An interesting, but extremely controversial theory was proposed in 1987 and had to do with the speed of light slowing down over time. The scientific community did not agree with these findings at all when it was first published. However, I have learned that new studies are being done on what is called C-DK, (or "c" the speed of light - decay). This theory suggests that when God created light in the beginning, it was infinitely fast. And since light is energy, it obeys the Second Law of Thermody-namics, and has been slowing down every since. (Setterfield 1987)

Evolutionists Address Their Problems With The Speed of Light and Determinations of the Age of the Universe.

In an article in the November 1992 issue of *Scientific American*, one of the most widely read scientific magazines in the country, astronomers were assessing their values for the Hubble constant (see section on Hubble), distance and time. The following quote is an example of some of their problems: "Our measurement and those of our colleagues have many implications for the age, evolution and fate of the universe. A low value for the Hubble constant implies an old age for the universe, whereas a high value suggests a young age...The age estimates for globular clusters are often cited as a reason for preferring, *a priori*, a low value for the Hubble constant and therefore an older age for the universe....A high value for the Hubble constant raises another potentially serious problem: it disagrees with standard theories of how galaxies are formed and distributed in space." This one quote points out many holes in their theory. First of all they understand the serious implications of the new cosmology and its effects on their basic theory. They are basing a value for the Hubble constant on an "estimated" age for globular clusters. Assuming an old age for these clusters, the astronomers chose a low value for the Hubble constant *a priori*, which means "fundamentally preferred". Therefore, they prefer this low value because it fits in with their standard theory. A high value for Hubble, meaning a young age for the universe, would severly disturb the standard theory. However, the science behind this assumption has holes in it big enough to fly the Starship Enterprise through.

Also from *Scientific American* in the May 1984 issue, Guth and Steinhardt, talking about the big bang and the origin of the universe, state "It is then tempting to go one step further and speculate that the entire universe evolved from literally nothing." Here they seem to be approaching the Creation Model for the origin of the universe.

This quote is taken from the March 1995 issue of *Discover Magazine* from an article discussing the state of the science of cosmology: "The field is in a troubled state, a disconcerting or an exciting one, depending on your personality—a state in which *even the most basic assumptions seem open to question*." (author's emphasis) The turmoil within this field is understandable when they are forced to consider that their most basic and cherished assumptions must be questioned and reevaluated.

The lead editorial by John Maddox in the August 10, 1989 issue of *Nature* deals with the growing problems of the Big Bang: " Apart from being philosophically unacceptable, the Big Bang is an over-simple view of how the universe began, and it is unlikely to survive the decade ahead." I believe we are seeing this happen even now. (Maddox 1989)

Planetary Astronomy — The Solar System   (Jones 1990)

Our Solar System is composed of nine planets orbiting our star we call the Sun. Within this system of planets there are smaller bodies such as moons (or satellites) of many of the planets, meteoroids, an asteroid belt, comets and cosmic dust. As the ancient astronomers observed the stars, it was noted that the stars had predictable paths across the night sky. The planets in our solar system are very much closer and move rapidly relative to the Earth and therefore do not have smooth paths in the sky. In fact some even appeared to move backwards in the night. The term planet comes from the Greek word for wanderer because of this strange motion. Thus they were given the name *planetos* or wandering stars.

Mercury — The innermost planet is Mercury whose size and appearance is similar to our Moon. Its 'day' and 'year' are so close that it rotates three times during two orbits of the Sun. The temperature on its equator at noon can reach $800°F$ and drop to $-292°F$ at night.

Venus — The second planet is closest to the Earth in size and comes nearest to the us. The surface contains mountains, plains, and highlands under a thick, dense layer of poison clouds of carbon dioxide. With a temperature over $750°F$ and an atmospheric pressure ninety times that of Earth, it is an inhospitable planet.

Earth — Our beautiful Earth that God created just for us to live on and to provide for our needs. Please read *Creation Geology: A Study Guide of Fossils, Formations and The Flood,* for an in-depth study of this amazing planet. Regarding our Moon, there have been many theories as to how in came to be, but I believe it was created on Day four as stated in Gen.1:14-16. I also believe that the rest of the entire solar system was created for the sole purpose of holding the Earth at just the perfect distance from the Sun and because God is infinitely creative.

Mars — Often referred to as the Red Planet due to its red color, Mars was named after the Roman god of war. The Martian day and axial tilt are similar to Earth. Giovanni Shiaparelli and Percival Lowell reported seeing canals on the surface, however later space probes proved they did not exist. They did show the existence of numerous volcanic shields, the largest being Olympus Mons. Mars has two moons, Phobos and Deimos.

Jupiter — The largest planet in our solar system has a volume over 1430 times the Earth and its mass takes up 70% of the combined mass of all the planets. Its vast size and extreme rotation of less that ten hours makes for incredibly violent storms on the surface, the most notable being the Great Red Spot No scientist has been able to determine why this storm stays in one spot since it was discovered by Cassini in 1665. Jupiter has thin rings and sixteen satellites.

Saturn — An incredibly beautiful planet with its rings and twenty-one satellites, Saturn is second in size to Jupiter. It has a rapid rotation of ten hours forty minutes, just a little slower than Jupiter. It has a mass ninety-five times the Earth, but a density of only 0.7 g/cm^3, which is less than water. Saturn consists of hydrogen and helium, and its divided rings contain particles ranging from a few microns to several meters.

Uranus — The seventh planet has a system of rings, fifteen satellites, and is composed mainly of hydrogen and helium. The most unusual feature of Uranus is its axial tilt of about $98°$, which means that it rotates on its side with its poles pointing toward and away from the sun for forty-two years.

Neptune — The position of Neptune was predicted by observations of Uranus, whose projected path was altered by the yet undiscovered planet. John Couch Adams and Urbain Leverrier independently calculated the probable location of this planet and it was located there by the Berlin Observatory.

Pluto — The smallest planet, consisting of frozen methane and having a moon, Charon, about half its size, is called a double planet by some scientists. Its very eccentric orbit places Pluto inside the orbit of Neptune for twenty years of its 248 year trip around the Sun.

Life on Mars — Science or Politics?

Sometimes science can be very unscientific, such as the claim by NASA in 1996 that scientists **believe** they have found **evidence** that life once existed on Mars. They have a piece of meteorite that they **think** came from Mars. These scientists **believe** that forty billion years ago a meteor hit Mars and kicked up little bits of the Martian surface into space. Then they **believe** that thirteen thousand years ago one of these bits landed here on earth.

There is a major question as to whether or not the mineral signature of this rock matches the mineral signature from Mars. The actual microscopic structures are less than one/one-thousandth of the diameter of a human hair. There is no life on earth that is anywhere near that small. The scientists say there is carbonate material in this rock. This same carbonate material is found in interstellar dust and many other meteorites that do not contain life.

This announcement, leaked to the media in the summer of 1996, is in this writer's estimation largely political, since NASA had suffered large budget cuts and needed a shot in the arm. The science behind this announcement was very **tentative**. The only accurate statement that was made during this announcement was that no one can be sure that there is life on Mars until a sample from Mars is retrieved and analyzed.

II. THE BIBLICAL STUDY OF ASTRONOMY

The Heavens Declare The Glory

" The heavens declare the glory of God; the skies proclaim the work of His hands. Day after day they pour forth speech; night after night they display knowledge. There is no speech or language, where their voice is not heard." (Psalm 19:1-3) Many scientists believe that the universe formed billions of years ago. Genesis 1:1 states, "In the Beginning, God created the heavens and the earth." This word for created means *out of nothing*. The stars supposedly formed from bits of stellar material coming together to coalesce into hot burning stars. The main problem is how do pieces come together after being blown out in all directions from a single point. Evolutionary scientists have no answer to this, but we know that God spoke everything in our orderly universe into existence in place and to function properly. "By the Word of the Lord were the Heavens made, their starry host by the breath of His mouth." Psalm 33:6

The Milky Way — Our own Milky Way Galaxy contains approximately 100 billion stars, and is about 100,000 light-years across. Astronomers say they can see 100 billion other galaxies beyond ours. They estimate the size of the visible universe to be from eight billion to twenty billion light years across. To put this into terms we can more easily relate to; we will shrink the Milky Way (100,000 light years across) down to one inch. The visible universe would extend for two miles in all directions with another galaxy every seven to nine inches. The galaxies, however, are not evenly spaced. There are large areas where there are very few stars, one is called the Great Void and there are enormous clusters of galaxies, one called the Great Wall. This is also an enigma for astronomers who would expect that the universe would be fairly evenly spaced out in many billions of years. Great clusters of galaxies are an indication that the universe is young.

The Milky Way can be seen as a band of light in the night sky. Our solar system is located two-thirds of the way out from the center or about 30,000 light years from the galactic center. There is a central bulge about 20,000 light years thick tapering out to the thin spiral arms. The Galactic center is located in the direction of Sagittarius. (Jones 2002)

Radio-Astronomers — Astronomers have discovered Quasars and Pulsars. Quasar is short for Quasi-stellar Radio Source, and a Pulsar is a short-period radio source. Radio-astronomers have been listening to the universe for only the last fifty years. Quasars and Pulsars are the stars that emit radio signals that the astronomers receive and study. Job, the oldest book in the Bible says that "at creation the stars sang." (Job 38:7) Could these radio-astronomers be listening to the echoes of creation?

THE GOSPEL MESSAGE IN THE STARS — God said that the lights in the sky were to be for signs. A sign is something that proclaims a message. The signs of the Zodiac were put in the heavens to proclaim God's message of salvation before He wrote the Gospel in the written form we call the Holy Bible. Christians have largely turned away from the study of the stars and the Zodiac because of the false teachings of astrology. The word Zodiac comes from the root 'zoad' which comes from the ancient Hebrew word 'sodi' which means a way, a path or a step. The zodiac pictures show the path or the *Way of Salvation*. These signs are the same for all nations and languages around the world and have been known as these very same things from the earliest days of mankind. These same twelve major constellations are found in ancient Rome, Egypt, Persia, Babylon, and China. The constellation stands for the same things even though the groupings of stars don't really look like the things they represent. This at the very least means that probably there was originally one source for the designations of the constellations. (Seiss 1972)

The Book of Job, the oldest book in the Bible written over 4000 years ago, speaks of the constellations. "Can you bind the beautiful Pleiades? Can you loose the cords of Orion? Can you bring forth the constellations in their seasons or lead out the Great Bear with its cubs? Do you know the laws of heaven?" (Job 38:31-33). God not would be pointing out the constellations if they were evil. God intended to present the Gospel message in His stars. There are not protogalaxies (not a newly forming galaxy) out there, there is "Protoevangelism," the first evangelism, the first preaching of the Gospel written there by God's hand, His handiwork that utters speech and shows knowledge! (Seiss 1972) "Yet when we analyze the evidence, the truth shines through the pagan distortions. For a student of the Bible the graphic symbols in the sky are unmistakable" (Peterson 2002).

Just look at the constellations! There, right in front of us, is the Virgin, the Mother and Child, the serpent, the King, a Crown, the serpent going after the crown, the Great Physician grasping the serpent, the serpent striking a man's heel, the dying sacrifice, and the living fish which is the symbol of the Church. There is an altar, an arrow, a Cross, a stream of water symbolizing the Holy Spirit being poured out into the fish's mouth, and of course the Lion triumphantly returning. Jesus was called "The Lion of Judah."

On the Fourth Day of Creation, the Gospel message was written by the hand of God in the heavens long before He wrote His Gospel on paper. This precious message is given to us by the book of nature as well as the Holy Bible, both written by the same Hand. The original salvation plan of God for His people was given to Adam in the Garden of Eden. I can just imagine God walking with Adam in the evenings, pointing out the constellations, and explaining everything to him. Then Adam would have passed that knowledge along to his sons and so forth. Arabic tradition says that Seth and Enoch were the original founders of the ancient understanding of the stars and their signs and the meanings of their ancient names. (Seiss 1972)

The twelve major signs move around the **ecliptic**, or the path the sun travels through the heavens. They are the twelve houses or tabernacles of the sun. Each one of them has associated with it three **decans.** The word decan comes from the word meaning *'piece'.* These minor constellations each tell a piece of the story and help to further explain the meaning of the major signs. Each major constellation takes up thirty degrees of the sky; and twelve times thirty equals 360 degrees of a complete circle. It is interesting to note that there are twelve chapters in the heavenly story, twelve months in a year, twelve tribes of Israel, and twelve Apostles.

The following descriptions of the constellations and the stars come from a wonderful book entitled *The Gospel In The Stars* written by Joseph A. Seiss. It was first written in 1882 and uses old style syntax, but it is absolutely engrossing reading. We highly recommend that you get a copy of this book and study it. ou can get it from from online book sellers or Kregel Publications, a division of Kregel, Inc., P.O. Box 2607, Grand Rapids, Michigan, 49501; their phone number is (616)451-4775. The following are brief synopses of each of the constellations, presented here with special permission from Kregel Publications.

Virgo - The Virgin

According to custom and to most authorities, the ancient zodiac begins with Virgo and ends with Leo. We start with the Virgin Mary and end with Jesus, the Lion of Judah. All traditional names and mythological names emphasize the virginity of the person represented in Virgo. Her names mean the virgin, the maiden, the maid of virgin pureness, etc. In one hand she holds a sheaf of wheat, the *spica*, the best of the seed, which is indicated by the brightest star in this constellation, **Al Zimach or Spica.** This indicates the Seed of Woman and speaks of Christ as the incarnate Son of God who will be 100% divine and 100% human. It is appropriate that Christ is represented as a seed of wheat and that He is known as The Bread of Life. In the other hand she holds a branch. The ancient names of the stars in this constellation emphasize the importance of the Branch. **Al Zimach** *means the shoot,* **Al Azal** *means the branch, and* **Subilon** *means the ear of wheat.*

The deacons that accompany Virgo are first Coma — Mother and child This constellation, the first decan of Virgo, denotes a pure virgin sitting on a throne feeding an infant boy who has a Hebrew name. Some nations call Him **Ihesu or Ieza** *which in Greek means Christ.* This woman is identified as the same woman in Virgo, and the child is identified with the Seed and the Branch. *The Hebrew word* **Coma,** *means the desired one, or the longed-for,* and is the same word used to describe Christ as "the Desire of all nations."

Then Centaurus — The half-man, half-horse The centaurs of legend were two creatures in one, just as Christ is both God and man having two natures in one being. The centaurs were supposed by the Greeks to be wise and powerful and immortal, but they were also depised by the people who considered them to be repulsive and hateful. The legend of the centaur, Cheiron, says that even though he was immortal, he willingly died so that his friend could live. The name of this constellation in *Hebrew means the despised.* The brightest star is called **Cheiron,** which is the Hebrew root for *'the pierced'.* Another star **Pholas,** *in Hebrew means the* *mediation or the making of prayer.* The star **Toliman** *means the heretofore and the hereafter,* and it is growing brighter in the sky. The Centaurus rides in the sky over the Southern Cross which is in the darkest part of the heavens.

Next is Bootes — The Coming One   The third decan is the figure of a strong man with a staff in his hand. This is a picture of the Good Shepherd looking over his flock. The Greeks confused this man with a ploughman, but the name of the brightest star in Bootes is **Arcturus** which is *the watcher or the keeper,* and **Arktos** is *the enclosure or the fold.* The star on the right side of Bootes is **Al Katurops**, which means *the Branch or the Rod* and is connected with the shepherd's staff.

Libra — The Balance Scales
The balance scales stands for fair payment, justice and equity. It denotes the required price paid for our sin by the blood of Jesus Christ. Christ is the Redeemer who paid the full price for sin. The name of this constellation in *Hebrew is* **Mozanaim**, *and means the scales, weighing.* In Arabic it is **Al Zubena**, *which is the purchase, or redemption, or gain.* In Coptic, **Lambadia** *means house of propitiation* and in Arabic, **Lam** *is graciousness and* **badia** *is the branch* — again showing the atoning grace of the Branch. The name of a star in one side of the scales of Libra is **Zuben al Genubi**, *the price deficient.* A star on the other side of the scales is **Zuben al Shemali**, *the price which covers.* Other names are **Al Gubi**, *heaped up high,* and **Zuben Akrabi**, *the price of the conflict.* One star is simply called **Tau**, the last letter in the Hebrew alphabet, which is written as a cross and signifies the end, the completion.

The first deacon is Crux — the Southern Cross   This constellation is distinctly defined by four stars in the form of a cross. It is no longer visible from the northern latitudes because of the gradual shifting of the earth; it was last seen in the horizons of Jerusalem at the time of Christ. It is a very striking configuration on the darkest part of the heavens. The Hebrew name, **Adom**, *means cutting off* , just as Christ was cut off from His Father as He took upon Himself all the sins of the world for all time. "It was placed there as the sign of what holy prophecy had declared should come, just as we reverence it as the sign of what has come in Jesus of Nazareth, the Virgin-born Redeemer of the world. It is the Cross of Calvary prefigured on the sky in token of the price at which our redemption was to be bought." (Seiss 1972)

The next is Victima - The Slain Victim   Christ was slain for our sins and is seen represented here as the slain victim. The victim is being pierced by the Centaurus who represents Christ, so we have the picture of our Lord sacrificing Himself. Jesus said that He laid down His life for His sheep and no man could take it from Him. Jesus was willingly slain for our sins because of His love for us and the Father willingly accepted His sacrifice as full payment for our sins.

The third deacon is Corona - The Crown   The third decan of Libra is the Corona Borealis, the Northern Crown, and it is vertically over Jerusalem once a month. This symbolizes the Lord Jesus, who willingly sacrificed Himself for us and is crowned King of Kings.

Scorpio — The Scorpion
The Arabic name is **Al Akrab**, which means *scorpion and also wounding, conflict and war.* The name in Coptic is **Isidis**, and means *attack of the enemy.* The main

star located in the middle of the constellation is **Antares** which means *wounding, cutting, tearing.* This sign symbolizes the mortal conflict and sets forth Christ as wounded for our transgressions. The tail of the scorpion is raised ready to strike as if to symbolize the bruising of Christ's heel.

The first deacon is Serpens - the Serpent   The serpent is seen going for the Crown, but being held and conquered by Ophiuchus. Satan took the form of a serpent in the Garden of Eden and is called the Dragon, the old serpent and the Devil.

The second deacon is Ophiuchus - The Serpent Holder   Here is seen the figure of a strong man wrestling with and defeating the serpent so that he does not get the crown. One foot of the man, by the scorpion's tail, is lifted up as if struck and the other foot is stomping on the head of the scorpion. Even though he is wounded he wins the conflict. This man is described as the Healer, the Physician, the Desired One.

The next is Hercules -   The Mighty One   In this constellation is seen the figure of another very strong man. He is down on his right knee with his foot lifted up as though it was wounded, another type of Christ. With his left foot, he is stepping on the head of Draco, the great dragon. He is holding a three-headed serpent in one jand and a club in the other. The Egyptian name for this sign means *Him who comes.* The brightest star in the constellation is in the head of the man and is called **Rash al Ghetto** which means *the head of him who bruises.* The name of the second star means *the Branch kneeling.* The Phoenicians worshipped a man called Hercules long before the Greeks heard of him. The Greeks liked the stories of the strength and power of this man, so they
incorporated him into their mythology.

Sagittarius - The Archer

In this sign we see the centaur again, who in all languages is known in this constellation as the Archer, the Bowman, or He who sends forth the arrow. He is aiming his arrow directly at the scorpion. This portrays Christ as the God-man and as the victor over sin and Satan. In the Book of Revelation, Jesus is described as a man riding on a white horse, the King of kings and Lord of lords, coming in righteous judgment to make war. This is the same picture we are given here in the sign of Sagittarius.

The first deacon is Lyra - The Harp   This constellation contains one of the brightest stars in the northern hemisphere, Vega. This figure of the harp, the oldest of the stringed instruments, denotes gladness, joy, and praise, praising the Archer for his achievements. **Vega** is the word from which we get our root word for *victory*, and it means *He shall be exalted, or The warrior triumphant.* Lucifer, before he was thrown out of heaven, was the leader of worship. Since then, the job of praise and worship of our God has fallen to us, the Church.

The next is Ara -   The Altar   The Greek word, **Ara,** means *a small elevation of wood or stone used as an altar for sacrifices or a funeral pile.* The Arabs call it **Al Mugamra,** meaning the *completing, the finishing.* The Greeks also used the word **ara** to *mean prayer.*

The final deacon is Draco -   The Dragon   Draco, the dragon, means the trodden down. The stars in this constellation also identify this as a dragon. **Al Waid** means *who is to be destroyed;* **Thuban** means *the subtle;* **Al Dib** means *the reptile.* The bright star in the serpent's head is **Rastsban** which means *the head of the Subtle,* *or the head of the Serpent.* Other stars are **Grumian**, *the deceiver;* **El Athik**, *the fraudulent;* **El Asiek**, *the humbled, brought down;* **Gianser**, *the punished enemy ;* **Ethanin**, *the long serpent.* The star, **Thuban,** in the second coil of the serpent's tail, used to be the Pole Star about 4700 years ago. The great worldwide Flood of Noah, was about 4500 years ago, during which time the earth's axis tilted. (For a detailed explanation of this please see the book *Creation Science: A Study Guide to Creation!* The pole star is now Polaris in the tail of Ursa Minor, which means not only the bear but also " the fold", which would be the Church. Satan lost his prominence, and the honor of having the pole star went to the Church.

Capricornus   —   The Goat

The figure of Capricornus has the front half of a goat that is fallen or dying, and the back half is a fish tail that is alive and wiggling. The goat is a sacrificial animal used by Moses in the desert as a sin offering. The names of the stars in this sign all point to this sacrifice: **Gedi**, *means a kid or a goat* and also *means the cut-off;* **Al Gedi**, *the kid;* **Deneb Al Gedi**, *the sacrifice comes;* **Ma'Asad**, *the slaying.* This gives the picture of the atoning sacrifice. It illustrates that through Christ's death we are made spiritually alive. Christ's atoning death results in new life for His church which took the sign of the fish as its symbol.

The first deacon is Sagitta   —   The Arrow   There is no bow associated with this arrow: it is in flight, sent from an unseen hand to do the work of the piercing and slaying of Christ.

The next is Aquila   —   The Pierced Eagle   Aquila is the pierced, wounded and falling eagle. It is another symbol of Christ dying for the Church. The brightest star in this constellation is **Al Tair** *which means the wounded.* The second star is **Tarared** which means *the scarlet-colored or covered with blood.* The names of other stars mean *the torn and the wounded in the heel.* Joseph Seiss describes the eagle in this way: "The eagle is a royal bird, and the natural enemy of the serpent. It is elevated in its habits, strong and swift. It is very careful and tender toward its young, and is said to tear itself to nourish them with its own blood when all other means fail. And here is the noble Eagle, the promised Seed of the woman, pierced, torn and bleeding, that those begotten in His image may be saved from death, sheltered, protected and made to live for ever." *(Seiss 1972)*

The third deacon is Delphinus   —   The Dolphin   The third decan of Capricornus is the figure of a lively fish jumping up. This symbolizes life springing up out of death of the dying goat. Again we see the symbol of the fish which was used by the early Church.

Aquarius   —   The Water-Bearer

This constellation is fascinating as it speaks of the joy of God's Spirit poured out on His people as the fruit of Jesus' victory. There is the figure of a man pouring water out of an urn that turns into a rushing stream. At the end of that stream is a fish, the Church, drinking in this blessing, as Jesus said He would do: "I will pour out my Spirit on all flesh". (Isaiah 44:3) The Greeks called him **Ganymedes**, *the bright, glorified, and happy one.* The main star on the man's right shoulder is **Sa'ad al Melik**, *which means the Record of the out-pouring.* The Greek and Latin names of this sign mean *the pourer forth of water, The exalted Waterman.*

The first deacon is Pisces Australis — The Southern Fish. Here is seen the fish, the symbol of the Church, drinking in the stream. Jesus said, "If a man is thirsty, let him come to me and drink"; (Rev.12:6) and we see that happening right here with the fish drinking in and being immersed in the heavenly waters of the Holy Spirit that are being poured out.

The next is Pegasus — The Winged Horse   The Greeks called this the horse of the gushing fountain. *Pega means the chief; and sus means horse and swiftly coming.* The names of the stars are *Markab, the returning; Scheat, he who goes and returns; Enif, the Branch; Al Genib, who carries; Homan, the waters; Matar, who causes the plentiful overflow.* All the names of these stars fit very nicely with the picture of Aquarius.

The third is Cygnus — The Swan   The swan is a beautiful bird held sacred by some civilizations. The bird is in flight with its wings outspread to form a beautiful cross. When this constellation rises in the evening it is know as Cygnus, but when it sets at dawn, it is known as the Northern Cross. The brightest star is *Deneb, which means, the Lord or Judge to come; Azel means who goes and returns; Fafage means glorious, shining forth; Sadr, who returns as in a circle; Adige, Flying swiftly; Arided, He shall come down.* These names symbolize the returning of the Lord.

Pisces — The Fishes

This constellation contains two fish which are headed in different directions. One is along the path of the ecliptic and the other is facing north. The two fish are bound together by a long cord that is being held by the foot of the Ram in the next constellation. The Hebrew, Arabic, Greek and Latin names for this sign all mean the Fishes. In Coptic, its name is *Pi-cot Orion, meaning the Fish, congregation, or the company of the coming Prince.* The two fish represent a multitude of people that would be the Church. One fish represents Moses and the Old Testament prophets who foretold the coming of the Savior, and the other fish represents the New Testament Church that came into being after Jesus came to earth.

The first deacon is The Band — the Bridle   The ancient name of this sign is *Al Risha, which means the band or the bridle, or unity.* Tying the two fish together shows us that the Old Testament Church of the Patriarchs is tied to the Christian Church. The understanding of the Old Testament and its prophesies helps the believer to more fully understand the fulfillment of the prophesies by Jesus and the hope we have as the New Testament Church. The Band that unites these two Fish is being held by the next sign, Aries the Ram or Lamb. This beautiful picture shows us that both parts of the Church belong to Christ, the Lamb of God.

The next is Cephus — The Crowned King   The next decan gives us the picture of the exalted Jesus, enthroned on high, wearing a royal robe, a crown of stars, and holding a branch in His hand. In His right shoulder is the bright star, *Al Deramin,* which means, *the Quickly-returning.* Other stars are *Al Phirk, the Redeemer; Al Rai, the Shepherd. The Egyptian name for this sign is Pe-ku-hor, which means the Ruler that comes.* The name *Cephus means the Royal Branch or the King.*

The last deacon is Andromeda — The Chained Queen   This is another picture of the Church as the Bride of Christ. But this woman is in chains, tied down by her wrists and ankles. This is the picture of the Church here on earth, tied down by the confines of this earthly existence. She will only be truly free when she is united in heaven as the Bride of Christ. The names of the stars in this sign, *Al Phiratz*, *Mirach*, *Al Maach*, and *Al Amak* mean the *Broken-down, the Weak, the Afflicted, and the Chained.*

Aries — The Ram

This sign is the Ram or the Lamb signifying the Lamb of God. Aries means *the chief or the Head;* Aryan means Lordly; Ram in English means high, great, elevated or lifted up. In Syrian the name means the Lamb; in Arabic it is called *Al Hamal, the Sheep, the Gentle, the Merciful.* The three main stars in the figure are *El Nath, the Wounded; El Natik, the Bruised; Al Sharetan, the Slain.* A triangle over the head of the Ram signifies its divine nature and the star *Ras al Thalitha* means, *the Head, or the Uplifted.*

The first deacon of Aries is Cassiopeia — The Enthroned Queen   This is the figure of a woman now sitting on a throne, a picture of God's Church lifted out of evil, no longer restrained by earthly bonds. She is enthroned on high with the Great King. The name *Cassiopeia, means the beautiful or the enthroned.*   The names of the stars in this woman are **Sheddar**, *the Freed*; **Ruchbah**, *the Enthroned, Dat al Cursa, the Seated.*   To the right of the Queen is *Cephus,* the Crowned King, holding his sceptre toward her as though to proclaim her his Bride.

The second is Cetus — The Sea Monster   This figure is the Leviathan of the Book of Job. A star of this sign is called *Mira* which means *the Rebel,* and is a variable star that shines brightly, then gradually becomes invisible about every three hundred days. This symbolizes Satan who is the Deceiver. The names of the stars in Cetus are *Menkar,* which means *the chained enemy;* and *Diphda, the Overthrown or Thrust-down.*

The next is Perseus — The Breaker   This sign is Perseus whose name means the Breaker. This man breaks the Deceiver and carries a sword and the head of Medusa. The names of stars in Perseus are *Atik, He who breaks; Al Genib, the One who carried away; and Mirfak, who helps.* The head he carries under his arm is that of Medusa, which means 'the Trodden under foot'. The name of the brightest star in the head is *Al Ghoul or Algol, which means the Evil Spirit,* and it is also a variable star which changes magnitude every three days. Names of other stars in the head are *Rosh Satan, Satan's head; Al Oneh, the Weakened, the Subdued.* Here altogether, we have the picture of the Lamb of God who breaks the power of the Evil One and raises His Bride to the status of the Enthroned Queen.

Taurus — The Bull

This figure of a rampaging bull signifies the glorious coming of our Lord Jesus Christ. This sign foretells that Christ will come in judgment like a rampaging bull upon the sinful world. Many ancient names of this constellation mean the Bull, even though it is not like any domestic bull, but rather is a wild, fierce bull with long horns, symbolizing Christ as an angry Judge. The Egyptian name for this sign means the Head, the Captain, the mighty chieftain who comes. *Al Deberan,* the brightest star located in the bull's eye, means *The Captain, Leader, or Governor.* It is interesting to note that this rampaging bull is rising up out of Aries, the Lamb of God. Riding on the shoulders of the bull is a grouping of seven stars called the *Pleiades*, representing the Church as in the Book of Revelation.

The first deacon is Orion — The Huntsman or The Glorious One   Here in this sign is a mighty hunter holding a lion skin in one hand and a club raised in the other. He is most easily identified by the band of three stars that make up his belt. From his belt hangs a sword with a lamb's head for the handle, and his foot is stomping on the head of Lepus, the enemy. The name of this very prominent and beautiful constellation is *Orion*, which means *He who comes forth as light, the Brilliant, the Swift.* In his right shoulder is a bright star called **Betelguese**, *which means the Branch coming.* On the other shoulder is **Bellatrix**, which means *Swiftly coming* or *Suddenly destroying.* In his foot that is stomping and crushing the Lepus is *Rigel, which means the Foot that Crushes.* The three bright stars in his belt are **Mintaka, Al Nitam, Al Nitah**, and are called, *" the Three Kings", or "Jacob's Rod".*

The next is Eridanus — The River of the Judge or the Fiery Stream from under the raised foot of Orion comes the Fiery Stream of the River of the Judge. Many times in the Bible we find reference to the River of the Judge or the Fiery Stream that issues forth judgment, and it is seen here flowing between Taurus and Orion.

The final deacon is Auriga — The Shepherd   In this third decan of Taurus, seated with the Rampaging Bull, the Mighty Huntsman, and the fiery River of Judgment, is pictured the Good Shepherd. This man is sitting on the Milky Way and is holding a mother goat and her kids in his left arm. *Auriga* in Latin means *a Conductor of the reins or coachman.* This man holds a band in his other hand that is the same band used to guide the Fishes and to bind the enemy. The brightest star in this constellation is *Capella* which lies at the heart of the mother goat. The forelegs of the goat are wrapped around the neck of the Shepherd. This is a beautiful picture of the Good Shepherd caring for His flock. The star in his right arm is **Menkalinon**, *which means the Band of the Goats or Ewes.*

Gemini — The Twins

Rather than two children being born at the same time, this sign of two people sitting together represents the union of Christ with His Bride. The first figure holds a club in his hand with his other arm around the second figure. The second figure is holding a harp in one hand and a bow and arrow in the other. The word Gemini in the original Hebrew does not mean two children born at the same time, but rather signifies the completion of a betrothal. The Coptic name *Pi Mahi means the United, the completely joined.* In the foot of the first figure is the star **Al Henah**, the Hurt, the Wounded. The Bright star in his head is called **Polluz**, which *means the Judge*, and is sometimes called Hercules, the Mighty Sufferer. In his waist is the star *Wasat* which means *Set, Seated or Put in Place.* The Egyptians called this figure *Hor or Horus*, which means *The Coming One, the Son of light, the Slayer of the Serpent, the Recoverer of the dominion.* In the head of the second figure is the star called *Castor or Apollo, which means the Coming Ruler or Judge, born of the light.* This sign then represents the marriage of the Lamb and the union of Christ with his Bride. Jesus is the Son of God; and since we who are the Church are called joint heirs with Christ and brothers of Jesus, we are also sons of God and in this sense the Gemini symbol could be Twins.

The first deacon is Lepus — The Hare or The Enemy   This sign is the figure of a rabbit or hare. In Arabic the name **Arnebeth** *means the Hare,* but it can also mean *the Enemy of the Coming.* In Egyptian the name is **Bashti-Beki** and means *the Offender confounded.* The names of the stars in this sign are **Nibal**, *the Mad;* **Rakis**, *the Caught;* and **Sugia**, *the Deceiver.* Remember that Orion is stomping on his head.

The next is Canis Major - The Great Dog   Canis Major is the Great Dog who is the devourer of the Hare. The main star here is Sirius, which is usually the brightest star we can see. **Sirius** *means Prince, Guardian, the Victorious.* The name of this figure in Egyptian is **Naz-Seir**, which means *the Sent Prince.* Jesus was referred to as the Nazarene. The names of other stars in this constellation are **Mirzam**, *the Ruler;* **Muliphen**, *the Leader, the Chieftain;* **Wesen**, *Shining, Illustrious, Scarlet;* **Adhara**, *the Glorious; and* **Al Habor**, *the Mighty.* Clearly here is a picture of the Victorious Christ.

The next is Canis Minor — The Second Dog   In Egyptian it is called **Sebak**, which means *Conquering, Victorious.* The name of the brightest star in this sign is **Procyon**, which means *Redeemed or Redeeming.* The second brightest star is **Al Gomeiza**, which also refers to redemption and means *burdened or enduring for the sake of others.*

Cancer — The Crab

The crab is known for its powerful claws that hold on tightly to whatever is in its grasp. As the crab grows, it must completely remove its old shell and grow a new one. When a person accepts the Lord as Savior, it is said that he puts off the old man or the old nature and puts on the new man who is clothed with righteousness. In the center of this constellation is a cluster of stars called the **Praesepe** *or the Manger.* In Hebrew and Arabic it means *the Multitude, Offspring, the Young, the Innumerable Seed.* In Latin **Praesepe** *means the place where the animals are fed, or the stable.* An interesting astronomical observation is that this sign of the Manger and the Northern Cross only appear in the sky together during the week around Christmas. As the constellation of Cygnus rises in the evening, it begins to travel across the lower part of the sky and turn upside down forming the Northern Cross. Then just before dawn during the Christmas Week, the **Praesepe** *or Manger,* rises above the horizon to be seen in the sky with the Cross.   What amazing wonders and signs the Lord has given us!

Egyptians call this constellation of the Crab, **Klaria**, *the Folds, the Resting-places.* We get the name Cancer from the Noetic word, **Khancer**. **Khan** means *the traveler's resting-place,* and **cer** means *embraced or encircled;* therefore, **Cancer** *means Rest secured.* Names of some stars are **Acubens**, *the sheltering, the good rest;* **Ma'alaph**, *assembled thousands;* **Al Himarein**, *the kids or lambs.* This sign then represents the eternal rest for the saints of God.   It shows Christ's possessions held secure, and assures us of God's fulfillment of His promise that He will have a great kingdom filled with a multitude of people from every race, tribe, and nation.

The first deacon is Ursa Minor — The Lesser Bear   The two constellations of the Lesser and Greater Bears were misnamed by the Greeks. The Egyptians, Persians, and the Indians all considered these two signs to be the flocks of God. The bright star in Ursa Major is **Dubeh**, *taken to mean bear; but the Hebrew word* **Dober** ,

28

which was the original name, actually means a *fold or collection of domestic animals.* This would be a very strange — looking bear with a very long tail. Taking the ancient Hebrew name, these two signs would be the Lesser and Greater Folds or Sheepfolds, symbolizing God's people, the sheep of His pasture. There are seven major stars in this constellation symbolizing the seven churches in Revelation, and it has a total of twenty-four stars, which suggests the twenty-four elders of Revelation. The names of the stars are **Kochab**, *which means the Star;* **Al Pherkadain**, *the Calves;* **Al Gedi**, *the Kid or the Chosen of the flock; and* **Al Kaid**, *the Assembled.* The Greeks also called this constellation **Arcas or Arx**, *which means the stronghold of the saved.* The pole star used to reside in the tail of Draco the serpent. But because the serpent lost its prominence, the pole star moved to Polaris, also called Arcas, in the tail of Ursa Minor, the Lesser Bear or the Lesser Fold, which is the Church. This change took place about the time of the worldwide Flood of Noah when the fountains of the great deep burst forth causing worldwide catastrophe on the earth. It was at this time that the axis of the earth began to tilt.

  The next is Ursa Major — The Great Bear   The names of the stars in this constellation further emphasize that the name of the sign should be the Great Sheepfold rather than the Great Bear. **Al Naish or Annaish** *means the ordered or assembled together as sheep in a fold.* **Mizar** *means guarded or enclosed place;* **Dubheh**, *herd or fold;* **Merach**, *the flock;* **Cab'd al Asad**, *multitude of the assembled;* **El Acolo**, *the sheepfold;* **Al Kaiad**, *the assembled;* **Alioth**, *the ewe or mother;* **El Kaphrah**, *the protected, the covered, the Redeemed;* **Dubheh Lachar**, *the latter herd or flock.* The seven main stars of this group are sometimes called **Aish**, *which means a community or a congregation.*

  The last is Argo — The Ship   This sign is associated with the story of Jason and the Argonauts, brave travelers returning home victorious. The brightest star in the constellation is **Canopus,** the name of the helmsman of the Argo, and which means *the possession of Him who comes.* Other stars are **Sephina**, *multitudinous good, the very abundance;* **Tureis**, *the firm possession in hand, or the treasure secured;* **Asmidiska**, *the travelers released;* and **Soheil**, *what was desired.* Here we have a portrait in the stars of the multitudes of saints returning to their heavenly home.

Leo — The Lion

  The earthly lion is known as the king of beasts. Jesus is known in Scripture as the Lion of the Tribe of Judah. The lion is always thought to be physically strong and fierce. The Lamb of God becomes the Lion tearing his enemies to pieces. This sign of the Lion is leaping forth as a consuming fire. In Jewish astronomy the twelfth sign was the sign of Judah, so Leo truly represents the Lion of the Tribe of Judah. Other names of this sign are **Aryeh**, *He who rends;* **Al Sad**, *He who tears and lays waste;* **Pimentekeon**, *the Pourer-out of rage, the Tearer asunder;* **Leon**, *the vehemently coming, the leaping forth as a consuming fire.* The main star is **Regulus**, which means *the feet which crush.* The second star is **Denebola**, which is *the Judge, the Lord who comes with haste.* Names of some other stars are **Al Giebha**, *the exalted;* **Minchiral Asad**, *the punishing or tearing of him who lays waste;* **Deneb al Eced**, *the Judge coming, who seizes or violently takes;* **Al Defera**, *the putting down of the enemy.* The names of the stars describe the Lion of Judah as He is described in Scripture - no mere coincidence.

      The first deacon isHydra — The Fleeing Serpent   The name *Hydra means the Abhorred.* The names of stars in this constellation mean that the evil serpent is finally taken out of the way. *Al Phard means the separated, the excluded, the put out of the way;* *Minchir al Sugia means the punishing or tearing to pieces of the Deceiver.*

      The next is the Crater — The Cup of Wrath   God said that His wrath would be poured out into the cup of His indignation. This constellation gives us the picture of this cup or bowl of wrath planted into the back of the Hydra, putting God's wrath squarely on the serpent.

      The final is Corvus — The Raven   The raven symbolized the bird of punishment. This bird is seen holding the serpent with its claws and tearing it with its beak. The Egyptian name for this sign is *Her-na, which means the Enemy broken.* Two stars in this raven are *Al Chiba*, which means *the Curse inflicted;* and *Minchir al Gorab*, which means *the Raven tearing to pieces.* All four of these constellations together prophetically assure us that Jesus shall be victorious over sin, and will totally vanquish the evil one.

CONCLUSION: Truly the heavens do declare the Glory of God. The orderliness and precision of the universe alone speak of the handiwork of God. But when you also consider that the stars were <u>placed</u> in Heaven, not just thrown there haphazardly by some explosion, it gives you some idea of the immensity of God's love for us. It is amazing to me that astronomers can look at these stars every night and have no understanding of the importance of the names of the stars. They are truly blinded.

      In Dennis Peterson's book *Unlocking the Mysteries of Creation* he explains how the mystery of the Sphinx has been revealed in the 4,000-year-old zodiac of Dende-rech, found in the ceiling of the portico of the temple of Esneh in Egypt. "There, between the signs of Virgo and Leo is a picture of the Sphinx, with the head of a woman and the body of lion. When we understand the divine story of redemption that begins with 'the seed of the woman' (Genesis 3:15) and ends with the triumphant lion (Revelation 5:5), the Sphinx makes sense."

      As Christians we need to take back the ground that Satan has stolen. Most Christians avoid studying the stars because of the association with the wickedness of astrology, but God created those stars and He designed them to speak and show knowledge of Him, and we need to get excited about the things that His creation can teach us.

                                          Jill Whitlock

Table of Planetary Data

Planet	Diameter (km)	Mean Distance From Sun (km)	Sidereal Period (year)	Axial Rotation Period (day)	Axial Tilt	Mean Density (gm/cm³)	Number of Satellites
Mercury	4,878	58,000,000	87.97 days	58d 15h 30m	0°	5.42	0
Venus	12,104	108,000,000	224.7 days	243d 24m 29s	178°18'	5.25	0
Earth	12,756	149,600,000	365.265 days	23h 56m 4.07s	22°30' - 23°24'	5.52	1
Mars	6,787	227,900,00	686.98 days	24h 37m 26s	25°12'	3.94	2
Jupiter	142,800	778,300,000	11.86 years	9h 50m 33s	3° 06'	1.31	16
Saturn	120,000	1,427,000,000	29.46 years	10h 39m 22s	26°42'	0.69	21
Uranus	50,800	2,870,000,000	84.01 years	17h 14m	97°54'	1.3	15
Neptune	49,500	4,497,000,000	164.79 years	18h 26m	29°36'	1.66	3
Pluto	2,300	5,900,000,000	248 years	6d 9h 17m	94°	1.8	1

Reference: Page 9 of "The Practical Astronomer" by Brian Jones, Simon and Schuster, 1990.

Creation Astronomy
Grades K-3

Objective: To study astronomy from a Biblical perspective through observation, comparison, research, and experiments.

Topics to study: The universe and how it began: Genesis vs. big bang theory, astronomers, lightyears, our solar system, stars, and constellations.

Outline

I. The Scientific Study of Astronomy
    A. Ancient Astronomers
        1. Copernicus
        2. Kepler
        3. Galileo
        4. Newton
    B. Big Bang Theory
        1. Explanation
        2. History
    C. Problems with the Big Bang
        1. Galaxy Clusters
        2. Comets
        3. Warm Planets
        4. The Sun
        5. The Moon
    D. Speed of Light
    E. Solar System

II. The Biblical Study of Astronomy

    A. The Heavens Declare the Glory
        1. The Milky Way
        2. Observing the Stars
    B. Gospel Message in the Stars
        1. Virgo
        2. Libra
        3. Scorpio
        4. Sagittarius
        5. Capricornus
        6. Aquarius
        7. Pisces
        8. Aries
        9. Taurus
        10. Gemini
        11. Cancer
        12. Leo

Lesson Plans

Ancient Astronomers

Subject	Monday	Tuesday	Wednesday	Thursday	Friday
Bible/Religion Studies	TS				
Astronomy Teaching Outline	Ancient Astronomers				
Reading Selection	AR	CR	AR	CR	AR
Vocab/Spell/ Grammar Language Arts	Assign 5-20 words from list or reading		Write or dictate sentences using words	Use sentences for parts of speech	Dictate or write paper on being an astronomer
Math Reinforcement		Choose K-3			
Science Activities and Experiments	Choose K-3		Choose K-3		
Geography/History Ideas		Locate Europe on World Map Name Continents		Ancient Explorers chart directions	
Art/Music		Sing Selected songs		Choose Art Activity	
Math: TS					
Reading Program: TS					

LA= Language Arts
TS= Teacher Selection

CR= Creation Resource: Read Selected Books from resource list or others
AR= Astronomy Resource: Other books that fit the topic

Lesson Plans

Subject	Monday	Tuesday	Wednesday	Thursday	Friday
Bible/Religion Studies	TS				
Astronomy Teaching Outline	Big Bang Explain		Big Bang		
Reading Selection	CR	CR	CR	CR	CR
Vocab/Spell/ Grammar Language Arts	Assign 5-20 words from list or reading		Open ended story		Dictate Story about why Big Bang is not true
Math Reinforcement		Count Days of Creation			
Science Activities and Experiments	Demo Big Bang		Science Activity Comets		
Geography/History Ideas		Choose K-3		Choose K-3	
Art/Music		Sing Selected songs		Choose Art Activity	
Math: TS					
Reading Program: TS					

LA= Language Arts   CR= Creation Resource: Read Selected Books from resource list or others
TS= Teacher Selection   AR= Astronomy Resource: Other books that fit the topic

Lesson Plans

Solar System 1

Subject	Monday	Tuesday	Wednesday	Thursday	Friday
Bible/Religion Studies	Genesis				
Astronomy Teaching Outline Planets	Solar System		Solar System		
Reading Selection	Creation		Sun/ Moon		Earth
Vocab/Spell/ Grammar Language Arts	Assign 5-20 words from list or reading		Dictate story about Creation		Choose LA activity
Math Reinforcement		Calendar			
Science Activities and Experiments	Solar System Model		Continue Model		
Geography/History Ideas		Use atlas		Choose K-3	
Art/Music		Sing Selected songs		Begin drawing Sun, Moon and Earth	
Math: TS					
Reading Program: TS					

LA= Language Arts   CR= Creation Resource: Read Selected Books from resource list or others
TS= Teacher Selection   AR= Astronomy Resource: Other books that fit the topic

Lesson Plans

Solar System 2

Subject Date:	Monday	Tuesday	Wednesday	Thursday	Friday
Bible/Religion Studies	TS				
Astronomy Teaching Outline	Solar System				
Reading Selection	Mercury/ Venus	Mars	Jupiter/ Saturn	Uranus/ Neptune	Pluto
Vocab/Spell/ Grammar Language Arts	Assign 5-20 words from list or reading		Cut pictures from magazine to illustrate words		Play Vocabulary Game
Math Reinforcement		Organize planets accord-ing to size Or math facts			
Science Activities and Experiments	Solar System Project		Jupiter Storms		Complete Project
Geography/History Ideas		Locate Europe on World Map		Choose K-3	
Art/Music		Sing Selected songs		Draw Constellations Observed	
Math: TS					
Reading Program: TS					

LA= Language Arts   CR= Creation Resource: Read Selected Books from resource list or others
TS= Teacher Selection   AR= Astronomy Resource: Other books that fit the topic

Lesson Plans

Milky Way/ Observing Stars

Subject	Monday	Tuesday	Wednesday	Thursday	Friday
Bible/Religion Studies	Psalm 19: 1-3		Job 38:7		
Astronomy Teaching Outline	Milky Way				
Reading Selection	CR		CR		CR
Vocab/Spell/ Grammar Language Arts	Assign 5-20 words from list or reading		Stepping Stars Game	Parts of Speech	Star Fishing Game
Math Reinforcement		Choose K-3			
Science Activities and Experiments	Milky Way		Learn to Observe Stars Use binoculars or telescope		Light Experiment
Geography/History Ideas		Geography and Stars		History of Space	
Art/Music		Sing Selected songs		Choose Art Stars	
Math: TS					
Reading Program: TS					

LA= Language Arts   CR= Creation Resource: Read Selected Books from resource list or others
TS= Teacher Selection   AR= Astronomy Resource: Other books that fit the topic

Lesson Plans

Gospel Message in the Stars

Subject	Monday	Tuesday	Wednesday	Thursday	Friday
Bible/Religion Studies	TS				
Astronomy Teaching Outline Gospel in the Stars	Virgo, Libra	Scorpio, Sagittarius	Capricornus, Aquarius	Pisces, Aries, Taurus	Gemini, Cancer, Leo
Reading Selection	TS				
Vocab/Spell/ Grammar Language Arts	Assign 5-20 words from list or reading		Open Ended Story		Review vocabulary
Math Reinforcement		Count Major Constellations			
Science Activities and Experiments	Identify Stars and Constellations		Identify Stars and Constellations		Identify Stars and Constellations
Geography/History Ideas		Chart Geographical Location of Stars		Choose K-3	
Art/Music		Sing Selected songs		Draw Constellations	
Math: TS					
Reading Program: TS					

LA= Language Arts   CR= Creation Resource: Read Selected Books from resource list or others
TS= Teacher Selection   AR= Astronomy Resource: Other books that fit the topic

Reading List
K-3

Read Aloud:
*These books contain Christian content and may be difficult to find in the library.

Adventures in the Solar System Planetron and Me, by Williams and Regan Price Stern Sloan Inc.: 1987, 60 pp. May be out of print. Order online. This is a fantasy adventure about a young boy who receives a toy model that turns into a space ship and whisks him off into space. The on-board computer teaches him factual information about all of the planets.

Adventures Beyond the Solar System Planetron and Me, by Geoffrey Wlliams, Price Stern Sloan: 1988, 62 pp. A transformer robot turned spacecraft brings a young boy to the outer reaches of the galaxy where he learns much about astronomy. May be out of print. Order online.

Men of Science, Men of God, by Henry M. Morris: Master Books: 2nd ed., 1988, 107 pp. Gives sixty-two biographical sketches of important scientists who believed the Bible.

The Astronomy Book, by Jonathan Henry: Master books: 1999, 80 pp. This wonderful resource will give you a Biblical Creation foundation to the stars and beyond!

The Magic School Bus Lost in the Solar System, by Joanna Cole.
Scholastic: 1989, 40 pp. Take a fictional ride with the "teacher" into space. This book will help children understand the scientific vocabulary because of the silly way the information is presented.

Voyage to the Stars, by Richard Bliss, Ed. D. Institute for Creation Research: 1991, 111 pp. A study of the stars from a Creation Scientist! This is a fictitious adventure story of astronauts and young space students who are learning about astronomy during a voyage on a space shuttle. The vocabulary is difficult for younger grades, but this book can be adapted with parental help.

Silent reading:
Finding Out about Sun, Moon and Planets , by Lynn Myring and Sheila Snowden EDC Publishing: 1982, 24 pp. Many pictures with captions that are very easy to understand. Explains difficult concepts in an easy manner typical of Usborne books.

My First Book About Space A Question and Answer Book, by Dinah L. Moche A Golden Book Western Publishing Co.: 1982, 24 pp. Answers basic questions in simple to read format. Some of the words may be difficult for under second grade.

Rockets and Satellites A-Let's-Read-and-Find-Out Book, by Franklyn M. Branley Harper and Row: 1987, 32 pp. A great book about activity above the earth. It has simple explanations and wonderful illustrations.

What is a Star? *A Just Ask Book*, by Chris Arvetis and Carole Palmer Field Publications Weekly Reader: 1988, 32 pp. A cute story told from the Wise Owl's point of view that asks simple questions about the stars, using a basic vocabulary for the beginning reader.

Activity and Experiment
Resource List
K-3

Find the Constellations by H.A. Rey
> Houghton Mifflin Co: 1976, 72 pp.
> This is an excellent book that shows pictures of the night sky with stars on one page and the line drawings of the constellations on the adjoining page. There are many questions and a quiz presented in typical H.A. Rey style. A great book

The Glow in the Dark Night Sky Book by Clint Hatchett
> Random House, Inc.: 1988, 21 pp.
> Contains star maps that will glow in the dark once exposed to light. The problem with this book is you need a flashlight to "recharge" the maps and flashlights will cause your pupils to shrink. (Dialated pupils let in more light and you can see better in the dark). This is still a helpful book and fun to use.

Genesis for Kids by Doug Lambier and Robert Stevenson
> Lightwave Publishing, Inc.: 1997, 160 pp.
> A fantastic book containing experiments geared to the days of Creation. There are specific experiments for astronomy that will fit beautifully into this unit study. Experiments topics include the universe, the sky, constellations, motion in the sky, galaxy (similar to our Jupiter experiment), and the solar system and more! Highly recommended for your library.

How the Universe Works by Heather Couper and Nigel Henbest
> A Readers Digest Book, Dorling Kindersley Ltd.: 1994, 160 pp.
> This book covers the Earth, Moon, Solar System, Sun, Stars and the Galaxies and beyond. There are many experiments, activities and explanations wonderfully illustrated with photographs. Some of the activities may be adapted for K-1.
.

Outdoor Science Projects for Young People by George Barr
> Dover Publications, Inc.: 1991, 160 pp.
> Originally published in 1959, this book encourages the child to observe his neighborhood, whether it is a city, suburb or countryside. There is a section devoted to observing the night sky which is excellent.

Ranger Rick's NatureScope Astronomy Adventures
> National Wildlife Fed.: 1989, 77 pp.
> An educators guide to teaching astronomy. Chock full of activities and repoducible sheets. This series may be found in the library.

Unlocking the Mysteries of Creation by Dennis Peterson
> Master Books, 2002, 240 pp.
> Long awaited sequel to his previous work. Beautiful color illustrations and easy to understand. This book is a must have for every home library. Topics covered are unlocking the mysteries of the early earth, evolution, original man, and ancient civilizations. An original CD accompanies the book containing more valuable information and a narrated slide show!

Vocabulary/Spelling List
Grades K-3

These words may be used as a base for any vocabulary or spelling list. You may want to add more of your own once you begin studying this topic. Use the words as *vocabulary only* for the younger children.

altitude	double star	Milky Way Galaxy	spectrum
asteroid	dust	moon	star
astronomy	earth rotation	NASA	star clusters
atmosphere	eyepiece	nebula	star finder
axis	focus	phase	star map
big bang theory	galaxy	prism	sun
binary star	Genesis	orbit	sun spot
binocular	gravity	oxygen	super giant
calcium	great red giant	planet	telescope
carbon dioxide	helium	planetarium	time zone
celestial	hydrogen	Polaris	universe
equator	light pollution	radiation	wane
comet	light-year	revolve	wax
constellation	magnetic field	rotate	white dwarfs
corona	magnitude	satellite	x-rays
crater	mass	solar system	yellow giant
degree	meteor	spectroscope	zodiac

Vocabulary/Spelling
and Grammar Ideas
K-3

Use the vocabulary words as spelling words. Here are some activities to help you incorporate the vocabulary words into your unit study.

ϒ Have children use the words in sentences to show the meaning. Younger children can use the words in sentences or stories. They can dictate them to an adult or older child who can write the sentences for them. Then have them "read" their sentences.

ϒ Have young children (K) pick out letters of the alphabet that they need to learn. Write the vocabulary words in large bold print on an erasable surface, or on paper. Have them circle the letter they are learning. (All the A's, B's, C's, etc.) Be sure to add your own *basic* words to the list!

ϒ Choose one or two of the children's "best" sentences and have them recopy them using their neatest handwriting. (Give them a model to copy if they are just learning to print or write.)

ϒ Use the sentences the child has written to label the parts of speech. Use colored pencils or markers for this activity. Color code each part of speech as follows:

Underline the *nouns* once in red.

Underline the *verbs* twice in blue.

Draw a green squiggly line under the *adjectives.*

Draw a purple box around the *prepositions.*

(Continue this pattern with any other parts of speech you are studying.)

ϒ Use the vocabulary words for younger children to make picture books. The children can cut pictures out of magazines or draw pictures to illustrate the words.

ϒ Make up short rhymes, For example: I have fun when I see the _____ (sun). The stars are so _____ (far).

ϒ Have the child look in the grocery store for as many "space" words as possible. For example: Chicken and *Stars* soup, *Celestial* tea, *Comet* cleanser, *Milky Way* candy bar, etc. Have the child keep an ongoing list of words, adding to them as each new item is found.

ϒ Have spelling or vocabulary "jumping" bees. (If you have more than one child, give each one words from his own list.) Each child starts at one end of the room. If he defines the word correctly, or spells the word correctly, he can take one of the following: two baby jumps, a one-leg hop, three little steps, etc. (make up whatever you wish!)   Children love this game. It's even a favorite with older kids. The child to reach the end first is the winner. (No-win version: the children compete against themselves, keeping track of words that are correct or incorrect.)

ϒ Make "stepping stars" using the vocabulary words. Take scrap paper, draw "stars," and write a vocabulary word on each sheet of paper. Spread the "stars" out in a pattern on the floor. The child takes a pebble or other marker. Using dice, roll a number. The child takes the number of "steps" shown on the dice, then reads the word on the "star" where he stops. If he defines the word correctly, he places his marker on the "star". The first to finish wins. Game variations: winner is the one who answers the most words correctly. Bonus points for child who can place stars in the pattern of the Big Dipper after the game is over.

ϒ "Starfishing" game: Cut out small starfish in various shapes and label each with one of the vocabulary words. (Have the children help with this activity!) Clip a paper clip to each "starfish". Tie a string to a magnet, and attach to a yardstick or dowel rod. Use the fishing rod to fish for words. The "fishermen" can keep the starfish if they can give the correct definition, spell the word, or tell what part of speech it is. The one who has the most starfish wins.

Language Arts Ideas
K-3

These suggestions may help you with incorporating language arts into your unit study.

♈ Read *The Magic School Bus Journey to Space.* Have your children pretend they are students in Miss Fizzle's class. What would they do or say on each page? Have them draw pictures of themselves and write down their comments. Read the book again including their comments! (Do the same activity with any other book of interest.)

♈ Tape record the above activity with the additional dialogue and sound effects.

♈ Choose a paragraph from one of the books you are reading on astronomy. Write this paragraph neatly and have the children copy it. Dictate the paragraph to older children once they have learned to spell the words. Have them check their own papers. (This may need to be practiced more than once.)

♈ Use different constellations and the original meanings of their names. Inventing as many creative descriptions as possible, take turns describing a constellation and have the others guess which constellation it is. For example, for *Virgo*, "This constellation represents the Mother of Jesus. It is at the beginning of the Hebrew Zodiac charts." (The modern Zodiac begins with January.)

Υ Have each child write a paper telling about his life as an "astronomer" or "astronaut". Have him tell why he chose this profession and what his greatest "experience" has been.

Υ Begin an open-ended story, and take turns adding to the story orally (this is especially fun with a group of different-aged children). For example: "One evening, while camping with some friends I was ready to call it a night and enter my tent. I was exhausted after a long day of hiking, yet I looked up into the bright, star-lit sky one more time. There to my amazement was a bright streak of light and what appeared to be a falling star heading right for our campsite! I quickly..."

Υ Use the above story with different variations. The places can be any of the geographical places you are studying. For example: While in the Rocky Mountains, Florida, California, etc.

Υ Write a paper naming all of the planets in the solar system and a brief description of each one. Approximately 200 words.

Υ Go on an evening nature hike (with your parents or other adult) and record everything you see that deals with astronomy. Are there any stars that appear to be brighter than others? Make sure you are in an area that does not have much light. Have younger children draw pictures to illustrate what they see. (See art section for more ideas.)

Υ Keep an evening nature diary. Record different things you see each evening out in nature. Draw pictures of what you see. (Parents can write for their younger children, or give them a tape recorder to record what they see!)

Υ Read a poem about stars and planets. Write a variation of the poem or write an original poem.

Υ Write about taking a trip into space. What did you take? Where did you go? What did you see? How fast did you travel?

Υ Make your own crossword puzzle. Write definitions for the vocabulary words. Give to an older sibling or parent to figure out.

Math Reinforcement
Ideas

ϒ Have the children organize the planets from smallest to largest. Is this the true order in which they are found?

ϒ Have the children categorize stars according to traits: super giant (very large and bright star), white dwarfs (almost burned out and dim), yellow giant (bright yellow star), etc. They can plot the results on a bar graph. *(See Voyage to the Stars on reading list)*

ϒ "Count" the days of Creation. Compare them to our calendar. Do the days of Creation fit with the days of the week?

ϒ Write down the number of miles from the Earth to the Sun. How many zeros are in the number? Can anyone walk that far? Why not? Walk one mile. How long did it take? How long does it take by car? Compare the various times.

ϒ What is the distance light can travel in one year? Write down this number. How many zeros are there? What is the place value of each of the various digits?

ϒ Show the concept of multiplication (or sets) by grouping "stars" in sets of 2, 3, 4, etc. Is it easier to multiply or add?

ϒ Show the concept of division by breaking up groups of "stars" (or Milky Way candy bars!) by the dividing the numbers evenly among several people. (Character trait of generosity!)

ϒ Make the solar system to scale. Use a ruler with precise measurements and draw on poster board, then cut out. Use the following (or make up your own!) diameters of the "planets": Mercury 3/8 in., Venus 1 5/8 in., Earth 1 5/8 in., Mars 3/4 in., Jupiter 19 in., Saturn 15 in., Uranus 8 in., Neptune 8 in., Pluto 1/4 in. Hang on a large stick or from the ceiling in a room. Note: The sun is not included in this model because it would need to be 13 feet in order to work with the above scale! (*How the Universe Works*)

ϒ Convert the inches in the assignment above to centimeters.

ϒ Make a coat-hanger balance with two paper clips at each end. Hang this from a door knob. Use the pictures of the planets made out of poster board above. "Weigh" the planets. Use other objects to weigh. Hang paper cups from the paper clips and place objects in the cups to weigh.

Science Activities and Experiments
K-3

Doing science activities and experiments is lots of fun! Using the scientific method makes it easier to understand. The **scientific method** is a procedure used to do an experiment in an organized fashion. The point of the scientific method is to solve a problem or further investigate an observation. (See page 2) Once you ask the question make sure the children give you their **hypothesis** (or "guess" for the younger children). This is what they think will happen. If they have no idea, read or observe to further research the question. The children can write (or draw) their experiment using the scientific method. **Parental supervision necessary! Always use caution when doing any science projects or experiments. Never look at the sun!**

ϒ Make a magnet. Stroke a large needle in one direction for several minutes on a bar or horseshoe magnet. Float the needle in a shallow container (margarine tub works well) of water. Which way does the needle point? The Earth has a strong magnetic field. You can show this by using a compass or anything that has been magnetized. Why doesn't the needle sink? (It does not break the surface tension of the water; this has nothing to do with the magnetic field!)

ϒ Find out which way is North without a compass. Place a stick in the ground in an open space where the sun is shining. Place a large piece of paper, poster board or newsprint rolls (large rolls may be purchased at school supply or office stores) on the ground at the base of the stick at noon (or 1 p.m. during daylight savings time). The shadow of the stick will point in the direction that is north. Mark the shadow of the stick on your paper. Which way would it point if you lived in the Southern hemisphere? Why is that? (Look at a globe to find out why.) (*How the Universe Works*)

♈ Find out why we can't see stars in the daytime. Cut out "stars" from yellow construction paper and glue onto a dark blue poster board. (Make the stars into patterns of various constellations if you wish.) Stand the poster board "sky" up in a vertical position. Cover a sheet of acrylic plastic (can be purchased in art stores) with tracing paper (this is the "atmosphere").   Place this six in. in front of the "stars". Shine a desk lamp or high-powered flashlight (the sun) on the stars. Can you see the stars through the "atmosphere"? Turn the lamp towards you. Can you see the stars now? (*How the Universe Works*)

♈ Observe light pollution. Compare the amount of light from artificial sources and its effect on your local area.   Take an evening drive into various sections of your town to observe the stars. Go to places that have a lot of light (like a downtown area or ball field). Compare these places to others that don't have as much artificial light (country or rural areas). Where can you see the stars the best? Are the stars visible in areas where there are many lights ? Use a local map to mark the spots that are the best places from which to observe the night sky.

ϒ Make a comet. Glue strips of different colored tissue paper onto one side of a small Styrofoam ball. Place a pencil into the bottom end (pointed side into Styrofoam). Hold the "comet", and using a hair dryer, blow "solar wind" at the comet (use a cool setting). What happens to the strips? Move the comet around and experiment with different positions while holding the hair dryer still. What happens to the tail? (A comet's tail points away from the Sun because of the effects of solar wind.) (adapted from *How the Universe Works*)

ϒ Recreate Jupiter's "storms". Take a bowl and place about a cup of milk (whole milk works best) in it. Drop in various colors of food coloring in the milk. Place one drop of dishwashing soap on top of each drop of food color. What happens? Watch the "storm". (*How the Universe Works*)

ϒ Experiment with light. What happens to white light when its rays are bent? Use a prism to find out. You can also use a garden hose in the sunlight and watch the sun as it filters through the drops of water. What do you see?

ϒ Why do meteors spread out? (*How the Universe Works*) Use the teaching outline for a "Creation Science" perspective.

ϒ Discover the magnitude of stars in the Big Dipper. (*Find the Constellations*)

ϒ Discover how the earth's rotation makes the sun appear to move in the sky. (*Ranger Rick's NatureScope Astronomy Adventures*)

ϒ Make a star chart. (*How the Universe Works*)

ϒ Create your own "big bang". Take a small paper bag and about 10 - 20 popsicle sticks. Inflate the bag and pop it. Do the popsicle sticks form a house (or any distinct pattern or design)? How do you get order from chaos?

ϒ Study the planets and their distances. Make a chart of their size and distance from the sun. (*Ranger Rick's NatureScope Astronomy Adventures*)

ϒ Find the stars using a star guide book. (*Stars A Golden Guide*)

Geography/History
Ideas
K-3

ϒ Make a large world map using large sheets of paper (computer paper taped together works well). Many newspaper companies sell newspaper remnant rolls for a minimal charge ($1.00). Use pieces of yarn to outline the continents. Star places where early astronomers lived.

ϒ Using the above map, locate and mark places where astronomy observation laboratories or telescopes are set up today. Why were these locations chosen?

ϒ Study and read about the different astronomers and scientists that made major discoveries. Talk about their contributions. You can do a mini-play; pretend you are the scientist telling another person about a great discovery. Perhaps you are the first person the scientist told about his discovery. Tell how he acted, and whether he was excited. Do this with several people.

ϒ How did early discoveries (such as the fact that the planets revolve around the sun) affect the thoughts of the day? Why were people affected?

ϒ How was gravity discovered? Is this a true story? *(Telescope Power)*

ϒ Use a globe and find latitude, longitude, and the northern and southern hemispheres. Discuss how the sky looks from the different hemispheres. Do all the sky charts you can purchase work equally well in all parts of the world? Why or why not?

ϒ Use the night sky to find the direction in which you are facing. Is this easy to do? Why or why not? Compare this to finding the direction when the sun is shining. Why is this easier?

ϒ What is the first mention in the Bible about the sky? The stars?

ϒ What star do you think led the Wise Men to find the Savior?

ϒ What were the different theories of how the solar system evolved?

ϒ Who discovered the first telescope? Why was this discovery important? Who do most people think invented the telescope? Why?

Art/Music
K-3

Music

ϒ Sing along with *Wee Sing Around the Campfire* (cassette with book)

ϒ Write your own words using the Gospel message in the stars and set them to the tunes of the songs in *Wee Sing around the Campfire* or other familiar tunes.

ϒ Sing "Twinkle, Twinkle, Little Star". Which star (or stars) in the sky do you think the song is talking about?

ϒ Play your choice of music and "twirl" around the "sun" the way the planets and moons do. One child can be the sun spinning clockwise and the others Venus and Neptune spinning counter-clockwise and traveling backwards!

Art

ϒ Go on an *evening* nature hike and take a drawing tablet with you. Draw the things that you see on your walk. Try to find the best place to view stars. Keep a nature drawing book. Research each drawing with a nature book and label the pictures. (Bring a star chart with you!)

ϒ Make different constellations out of clay dough (or anything else you wish!). *Recipe for clay dough:* four cups of flour, one cup of salt, one and one half cups of water. Add more flour if it's too sticky. Knead six minutes! Shape, then bake at 325°-350° until slightly brown.

ϒ Make a 3-D model of the solar system. Use clay (from the previous activity). Color the dough different colors for each of the planets. Place them on a board and have your parents guess what planets they are. Use a book to help you place the planets in the correct positions.

ϒ Make *finger-paint,* and use it to illustrate a story or paint something seen on a starry night.   Whip soap flakes (any brand) and water together until creamy. Add powdered tempera paint, or food coloring, to tint different colors. (Be careful, food coloring stains!)

ϒ Make a model of history from the beginning of time (use the Bible to help you with a time line). Use pieces of poster board and draw out the days of Creation. Pay special attention to when the stars were created! Use yarn or string to hang your pictures up.

ϒ Make a model of the planets (see page 48 for dimensions or make up your own). Color the planets using a science book to help you.

Creation Astronomy
Grades 4-8

Objective: To study astronomy from a Biblical perspective through observation, comparison, research and experiments.

Topics to Study: The universe and how it began, Genesis vs. big bang theory, astronomers, speed of light, solar system, stars, constellations, and the Gospel message in the stars.

I. Scientific Study of Astronomy
- A. Ancient Astronomers
    1. Greeks
    2. Copernicus
    3. Brahe
    4. Kepler
    5. Galileo
    6. Newton
- B. Big Bang Theory
    1. Explanation
    2. History
- C. Problems for the Big Bang Theory
    1. Galaxy Clusters
    2. Spiral Arms
    3. Comets
    4. Warm Planets
    5. The Sun
    6. The Moon
- D. The Speed of Light
    1. The Speed of Light Today
    2. The Speed of Light and the Six Days of Creation
- E. Solar System

II. Biblical Study of Astronomy

- A. The Heavens Declare the Glory
    1. The Milky Way
    2. Observing the Stars
- B. Gospel Message in the Stars
    1. Virgo
    2. Libra
    3. Scorpio
    4. Sagittarius
    5. Capricornus
    6. Aquarius
    7. Pisces
    8. Aries
    9. Taurus
    10. Gemini
    11. Cancer
    12. Leo

Lesson Plans

Astronomers

Subject	Monday	Tuesday	Wednesday	Thursday	Friday
Bible/Religion Studies	TS				
Astronomy Teaching Outline Ancient Astronomers	Ancient Astronomers	Ancient Astronomers			
Reading Selection	TS				
Vocab/Spell/ Grammar Language Arts	Assign 10-30 words from list or reading		Find articles in newspaper relating to astronomy		Review vocabulary
Math Reinforcement		What is a light year?			
Science Activities and Experiments	Ancient Astronomer Tables		Continue charting		TS
Geography/History Ideas		Research astronomers		Study geographical locations of Astronomers	
Art/Music		Music: Sounds in space		Use vocabulary words for word art	
Math: TS					
Literature					

LA= Language Arts   CR= Creation Resource: Read Selected Books from resource list or others
TS= Teacher Selection   AR= Astronomy Resource: Other books that fit the topic

Lesson Plans

> ## *Big Bang Theory and Problems*

Subject	Monday	Tuesday	Wednesday	Thursday	Friday
Bible/Religion Studies					
Astronomy Teaching Outline Big Bang/Problems	Big Bang Explanation	History	Problems	Speed of Light	Speed of Light Creation
Reading Selection	Secular sources Big Bang	Creation sources Big Bang	TS	TS	TS
Vocab/Spell/ Grammar Language Arts	Assign 10-30 words from list or reading		Open ended story using some new words		Grammar assignment using words
Math Reinforcement		Speed of light equations			
Science Activities and Experiments	Big Bang Activity		Infrared Light experiment		Demonstrate refracting light
Geography/History Ideas		Atlas: Find Hemispheres		TS	
Art/Music		Stain glass design		Noted musicians	
Math: TS					
Literature					

LA= Language Arts
TS= Teacher Selection

CR= Creation Resource: Read Selected Books from resource list or others
AR= Astronomy Resource: Other books that fit the topic

Lesson Plans

Solar System 1

Subject	Monday	Tuesday	Wednesday	Thursday	Friday
Bible/Religion Studies					
Astronomy Teaching Outline Solar System	Solar System				
Reading Selection	Secular sources solar system	Creation sources: solar system	Sun/Moon	TS	Earth
Vocab/Spell/ Grammar Language Arts	Assign 10-30 words from list or reading		Journal writing nature walk in evening		Play vocabulary game
Math Reinforcement		Chart planets and compare dimensions			
Science Activities and Experiments	Measure solar energy		Measure diameter of the moon		Demonstrate that the earth is round
Geography/History Ideas		Historic space exploration vehicles		Study space explorers	
Art/Music		Stained glass picture of solar system		Make own space music	
Math: TS					
Literature					

LA= Language Arts   CR= Creation Resource: Read Selected Books from resource list or others
TS= Teacher Selection   AR= Astronomy Resource: Other books that fit the topic

Lesson Plans

Subject	Monday	Tuesday	Wednesday	Thursday	Friday
Bible/Religion Studies					
Astronomy Teaching Outline Solar System	Solar System				
Reading Selection	Mercury/ Venus		Mars/Jupiter/ Saturn		Uranus/ Neptune/ Pluto
Vocab/Spell/ Grammar Language Arts	Assign more words		Write sentences		Secret code vocabulary activity
Math Reinforcement		Log mathe-matical facts about planets			
Science Activities and Experiments	Demo: Weightlessness in Space		Demonstrate centrifugal force		Make a solar system
Geography/History Ideas		History of Space Travel			
Art/Music		Work on solar system model		Space movies listen to sound-track and iden-tify instruments	
Math: TS					
Literature					

LA= Language Arts
TS= Teacher Selection

CR= Creation Resource: Read Selected Books from resource list or others
AR= Astronomy Resource: Other books that fit the topic

Lesson Plans

Milky Way/ Star Observation

Subject	Monday	Tuesday	Wednesday	Thursday	Friday
Bible/Religion Studies	Psalm 19:1-3		Job 38:7		
Astronomy Teaching Outline Milky Way	Milky Way	Milky Way			
Reading Selection	CR	AR	Star Observation		
Vocab/Spell/ Grammar Language Arts	Assign words from list or reading		Open ended story		Fact and Opinion Activity
Math Reinforcement		Measure angle of refraction of colors			
Science Activities and Experiments	Prepare for star observations		Demonstrate use of binoculars		Demonstrate use of telescope
Geography/History Ideas		Ancient Explorers used sky to navigate			
Art/Music		Complete other activities		Time line of composers	
Math: TS					
Literature					

LA= Language Arts
TS= Teacher Selection

CR= Creation Resource: Read Selected Books from resource list or others
AR= Astronomy Resource: Other books that fit the topic

Lesson Plans

Gospel Message in the Stars

Subject	Monday	Tuesday	Wednesday	Thursday	Friday
Bible/Religion Studies	TS				
Astronomy Teaching Outline Gospel in the Stars	Virgo, Libra	Scorpio, Sagittarius	Capricornus, Aquarius	Pisces, Aries, Taurus	Gemini, Cancer, Leo
Reading Selection	TS				
Vocab/Spell/ Grammar Language Arts	Review words		Write your own version of Gospel in Stars		Chart Constellations found
Math Reinforcement					
Science Activities and Experiments	Identify Stars and Constellations		Identify Stars and Constellations		Identify Stars and Constellations
Geography/History Ideas		Atlas: Hemispheres Chart Constellations		TS	
Art/Music		Draw Constellations		Read about musicians 1600's	
Math: TS					
Literature					

LA= Language Arts
TS= Teacher Selection

CR= Creation Resource: Read Selected Books from resource list or others
AR= Astronomy Resource: Other books that fit the topic

Reading List 4-8

*Books with strong Christian content may be difficult to find in the library.

Halley: Comet 1986, by Franklyn Branley Dutton: 1983, 32 pp.
     This is a book that discusses Halley's Comet, which was visible to us in 1986. It is interesting to read because it gives historical background on this and other famous comets.

*Isaac Newton: Mastermind of Modern Science, by David C. Knight. Franklin Watts: 1961, 55 pp
     Isaac Newton contributed much to science, not only in the discovery of gravity. This book is about his life and his contributions.

*Johannes Kepler: Giant of Faith & Science Sower Series: 1981, 202 pp.
     This book is written from a Christian perspective and tells about the discoveries, struggles and triumphs of Kepler's life.

*Men of Science, Men of God, by Henry M. Morris Master Books: 2nd ed., 1988, 107 pp.
     Gives 62 biographical sketches of important scientists who believed the Bible.

Pulsars and Black Holes in Space by Melvin Berger Putnam's & Sons: 1977, 80 pp.
     This book is written from a secular perspective but has done a good job in simplifying a complicated subject. It should be compared to the Teaching Outline.

Rediscovering Astronomy, by Eugene Provenzo Oak Tree: 1980, 88 pp.
     Discusses the history of astronomy and aspects of famous discoveries. Includes details on building a sundial, quadrant, sextant and telescopes.

*Voyage to the Stars, by Richard Bliss, Ed. D. Institute for Creation Research: 1991, 111 pp.
     Finally, a study of the stars from a Creation Scientist! This is a fictitious adventure story of astronauts and young space students who are learning about astronomy during a voyage on a space shuttle.

*Johannes Kepler: Giant of Faith & Science Sower Series: 1981, 202 pp.
     This book is written from a Christian perspective and tells about the discoveries, struggles and triumphs of Kepler's life.

The Magic School Bus Lost in the Solar System Scholastic: 1989, 40 pp.
     This book is referenced in the K-3 section and is highly recommended for grades 4-6.

*Men of Science, Men of God, by Henry M. Morris Master Books: 2nd ed., 1988, 107 pp.
     Gives 62 biographical sketches of important scientists who believed
the Bible.

Pulsars and Black Holes in Space by Melvin Berger Putnam's & Sons: 1977, 80 pp.
     This book is written from a secular perspective but has done a good job in simplifying a complicated subject. It should be used with a parent's guidance and compared to the Teaching Outline.

Rediscovering Astronomy, by Eugene Provenzo Oak Tree: 1980, 88 pp.
     Discusses the history of astronomy and aspects of famous discoveries. Includes details on building a sundial, quadrant, sextant and telescopes.

Activity and Experiment
Resource List
4-8

Astronomy for Every Kid by Janice Van Cleave
  John Wiley & Sons, Inc. 1991
  Great activities and experiments. Easy to do and they work! Many topics are similar to the ones covered in this book.

Bill Ney The Science Guy's® Big Blast of Science
  Addison-Wesley Pub.: 1993, 172 pp.
  This book written from a secular perspective states that Astrology is not a science and makes very little sense! Yet, Bill Ney falls short by his belief in evolutionary principles (ie: billions of years). This book contains many experiments and activities in the various fundamentals of science and space.

Genesis for Kids by Doug Lambier and Robert Stevenson
  Lightwave Publishing, Inc.: 1997, 160 pp.
  A fantastic book containing experiments geared to the days of Creation. There are specific experiments for astronomy that will fit beautifully into this unit study. Highly recommended for your library.

How the Universe Works by Heather Couper and Nigel Henbest
  A Reader's Digest Book, Dorling Kindersley Ltd.: 1994, 160 pp.
  A complete review is in the K-3 section. The experiments are easy to follow and can be done with minimal preparations for the most part. This series of books is among my favorites.

Ranger Rick's NatureScope Astronomy Adventures
  National Wildlife Fed.: 1989, 76 pp.
  An educator's guide to teaching astronomy. There are many activities dealing with the Solar System, Universe, Constellations and much more. Geared for K-6 and available at most libraries.

Telescope Power: Fantastic Activities & Easy Projects for the Young Astronomer, by Gregory Matloff
  John Wiley & Sons, Inc.: 1993, 119 pp.
  This book contains information about the early astronomers and the history of the telescope. It is informative even if it has a secular viewpoint. It features Copernicus, Brahe, Kepler, Galileo, and Newton. Great ideas for activities and experiments.

Unlocking the Mysteries of Creation by Dennis Peterson
  Master Books, 2002, 240 pp.
  Long awaited sequel to his previous work. Beautiful color illustrations and easy to understand. This book is a must have for every home library. Topics covered are unlocking the mysteries of the early earth, evolution, original man, and ancient civilizations. An original CD accompanies the book containing more valuable information and a narrated slide show!

66

Vocabulary/Spelling List

4-8

This list is to be used as a basis for your vocabulary and spelling words for this unit study. Look at the list of words given for grades K-3. If there are any words that your child does not know, add them to the list below. If you feel some words are too difficult, exclude them. If the child does not know the meaning of the words, have him look them up in a dictionary, or encyclopedia, and write a brief definition.

absorption line	cosmic ray	heliocentric	reflection
acceleration	dark matter	latitude	refraction
altitude	declination	lens	refractor
aperture	Doppler effect	longitude	resolution
asteroid	earth shine	lunar eclipse	revolution
astrolabe	eclipse	magnification	solar eclipse
astrology	ellipse	magnitude	solar flare
astronomical unit	elliptical galaxy	meteorite	solar wind
aurora	electron	nebula	spiral galaxy
big crunch	equinox	nova	stratosphere
binary system	eyepiece	observatory	supernova
binoculars	finder scope	objective lens	telescopic planets
black hole	field of view	ozone	ultraviolet light
boresight	flyby	parallax	umbra
brown dwarf	focal length	photon	wavelength
celestial sphere	focus	pulsars	wave velocity
centrifugal force	frequency	pupil	white dwarf
chromosphere	gamma ray	quasar	zenith
color filter	gas giant planet	red-shift	
conjunction	geocentric		

Vocabulary/ Spelling and Grammar Ideas
4-8

Use vocabulary and spelling words interchangeably in the following activities:

ϒ Use the words in sentences showing their meaning. Use the sentences the child has written to study the parts of speech. Continue the list below with any of the parts of speech you are currently studying. For example:

Underline a noun once.

Underline a verb twice.

Put a squiggly line under an adjective.

Put two squiggly lines under an adverb.

Put a box around a preposition.

Circle a pronoun with a "P" above it.

Highlight direct and indirect objects.

ϒ Use colored pencils or markers for the grammar activity, assigning a color to each of the parts of speech.

ϒ Choose the "best" sentences (usage) and have the children practice their handwriting skills by copying them.

ϒ Have the children make vocabulary cards. Use index cards; on one side write the word, on the other the definition. Use the words in different games.

ϒ Use the vocabulary words to play "hopscotch." Take chalk and draw a hopscotch grid outdoors (or make one indoors by marking out large squares with colored yarn). Lay one vocabulary card, word side up, on each square. Play hopscotch. In order to keep the card, the child must give the correct definition of the word in the square in which he lands. Continue to put more cards in the spaces as they are used up. When all the cards have been used, the child with the most cards wins.

ϒ Use the vocabulary cards to play the "jumping bees" or "stepping stars" games. Don't be surprised if your older children want to play.   Mine do!

ϒ Give each letter of the alphabet a secret code. Have each of the children write several difficult vocabulary words (ones they may be having trouble with) in secret code. Have them put all the words on scraps of paper. Put them in a bag and pull them out randomly. Try to decipher the words.

ϒ Study the Greek and Latin origins of words. For example "tele" means device for seeing. *(English from the Roots Up)*

Language Arts Ideas
4-8

♈ Begin an open-ended story and take turns adding to the story orally in a group. (This is especially fun with a group of different-aged children). For example: "It had always been my dream to be on a space-shuttle mission. As I checked the instrument panel which contained a computer display, I still couldn't believe I had actually been chosen from thousands of students. There were two students and six adults on board; my job was to monitor the computer screen which was focused on the constellation Orion. It worked automatically, taking pictures as our space ship hurtled through the sky. All of a sudden...!"

♈ Use the above story with different variations. The constellation can be any of the ones you are studying; you can change the mission of the trip, or even the fact that the main character is a student.

♈ Use a paragraph from one of the books you are reading on astronomy to give dictation. Check for proper spelling and punctuation.

♈ Use the star chart in the back of this book and write a version of the Gospel in the stars for younger children, be sure to illustrate your book.

Υ Research the difference between astronomers, and astrologers. In what ways are they similar? In what major ways are they different? Or, research the difference between astronomers and astronauts.

Υ Go on an evening nature hike and write a journal of your observations. Remember to write the location, day, time, and the name and description of each object you observed.

Υ Write different types of poems about stars, constellations, comets, etc.

Υ Study the word origin of the names of the constellations. Write a comparison of the original meaning of the words and the commonly "accepted" meaning of the words today.

Υ Read several books on astronomy. Choose different chapters of the books to check for comprehension by using any of the following ideas: identify the main idea, give the book a better title, infer beyond what is specifically stated, identify the correct sequence of events, identify facts and fiction, identify facts and opinions, or briefly outline the book.

Υ Take five or six sentences from a book you are reading. For example: "Many scientists have looked for evidence of a changing light speed, without success." (Astronomy and the Bible). Use a sheet of notebook paper and make four headings, labeling them: who, what, where, and when. Using the selected sentences answer those questions by writing a portion of the sentence under the specific topic heading.

ϒ Write a paragraph or two discussing why you do or do not agree with the Creation Scientists' findings about the universe. For example: what are the facts that point to a young earth? What does the red-shift have to do with the expansion-of-the-universe theory? What do Creationists and Evolutionists have to say about red-shift?

ϒ Divide a sheet of paper into two columns. Label the headings Facts vs. Opinions. Under the two headings, list as much data as you can find that has to do with astronomy and space.

ϒ Find articles in the newspaper or magazines that deal with astronomy-related topics. Ask questions about each article when you have finished reading it. If the article contains material contrary to Creationists' viewpoint, consider writing a letter to the editor using a well-researched article with quotes from various scientists to substantiate your point. Check punctuation and grammar! Submit your age when responding to the article.

Math Reinforcement Ideas
4-8

Υ What are some mathematical facts relating to the planets? (For example, the earth spins around once every twenty-four hours.) Chart these figures.

Υ What is a light-year? What distances in space are measured in light-years? Convert the light-year measurements to miles and AU (Astronomical Units).

Υ Make a chart of the planets and compare their diameters, mass, density and time it takes to orbit the sun.

Υ Measure the diameter of the moon. The next time a full moon appears use a tape measure, hold it at arm's length and measure the width of the moon. (You may need some help in doing this). Repeat this in one hour. Did your measurements change?

Υ Study the principles of a parallax. (An apparent shift in position of a star against the background of space.) A small shift indicates a star is further away, a larger shift indicates a star is closer. This can be used to calculate distances of stars using geometry. (How the Universe Works)

ϓ Measure the angle of refraction for the different colors of a light spectrum. Use a prism to break apart the visible light into the color spectrum. Put a blank sheet of paper under a prism and draw the angles; label the different colors. Measure the angles.

ϓ On graph paper plot the movements of the planets Earth and Mars. This will help in understanding how orbits relate to what you see in the night sky. Place the Sun in the center. Draw a small circle around the Sun, which will be the orbit of Earth, and a larger circle, which will be the orbit of Mars. Divide each circle in half through the center and through the circle until each circle is divided into eight equal divisions. Number each division sequentially starting with zero and ending with seven. Use a dime to represent Mars, and a nickel to represent Earth. Place the Mars marker on the number one; place the Earth marker on the number two. Draw a line between these points. If you were standing on Earth, the projection of the line would correspond to the starting point of Mars in your sky. Mars takes about twice as long as the Earth to orbit the Sun. *(Telescope Power)*

ϓ Light moves in waves similar to ocean waves. If you live near a beach, try to measure the frequency of the waves as they hit the beach. Use a stopwatch and time the waves as they reach the shore; next use a yardstick and try to measure the distance between a crest and crest of the wave that follows. This distance is called a wavelength. Chart your results.

Science Activities and Experiments
4-8

A good understanding of the scientific method is a must at this grade level! For an overview of the scientific method see the introduction page vi. Remember to formulate your question and hypothesis before you begin the experiment! At this age give the children flexibility to experiment. If they have an idea of something they want to try, give them the time to do it. It is helpful if they write out their procedures using the scientific method sheets (see page 167). In the event that they invent something, they will be able to duplicate the experiment!! **Always use caution when doing any science projects and experiments. Parental supervision necessary! Remember: Never look at the sun!**

Υ Measure solar energy. You will need several Styrofoam cups, black ink, red, blue, and green food coloring, water and a thermometer. Mix each food coloring and ink in a cup with approx. 50 ml. of water that is several degrees cooler than the outside air. Record the temperature. Place each cup in the sun and tilt it until the sun's rays shine into the cup. Make sure there are not any shadows. Record the time you turn the cup toward the sun. Leave the cups in the sun until the temperature (after stirring) reaches far above the temperature it was when you began. Record the temperature. Place cups in a shady place. When the temperature goes down, record the time that has elapsed. What was the change in temperature? How long was the water in the sunlight? To measure the area of water exposed to sunlight, mark the cup at the water level height. Use scissors to cut off the top of the cup, measure the diameter. The area of water surface equals the square of the radius of the circle (radius = ½ of the diameter) times pi (3.14) What was the area of the water surface on which the sunlight fell? (*Projects in Space Science*)

ϒ Measure the diameter of the moon! Next time the full moon appears large (when it is low on the horizon), use a tape measure, hold it at arm's length and measure the width of the moon. Repeat this every hour for up to four to six hours. Is there a change in size? Chart your findings. Do this several times during various seasons. Is there a change in the position of the moon? Is there a change in the size of the width of the moon?

ϒ The ancient astronomers made tables of the positions of the sun, moon and earth to accurately predict eclipses of the sun and moon. Create such a table by observing and recording these positions over a period of time. Can you predict the next eclipse?

ϒ Demonstrate centrifugal force. Take a small net or piece of cloth and wrap a ball (or similar object) in it. Tie this to a piece of string. Twirl the string in a circular motion above your head. (This is a good project to do outdoors.) Slow down the rotation. What happens to the ball?

Ϋ Variation: (Do this outdoors.) What happens if you release the string while the ball is spinning overhead at a fast speed? What does this demonstrate?

Ϋ Study electromagnetic waves. Use a science dictionary to find a model to draw. Label each wave, the wavelength, the direction of the wave and the magnetic field. *(The Usborne Illustrated Dictionary of Science)*

Ϋ Do an experiment demonstrating refracting light in our atmosphere. Take a one gallon glass container and fill it with water. Add six tablespoons of a household disinfectant and shake well. This will cause the water to contain tiny particles. The water represents the atmosphere. Here are three different experiments; make sure to ask your question and form a hypothesis before you begin! Using a poster board as a background, place the gallon jug in front of it. Shine a flashlight through the jug (atmosphere). What colors appear on the poster board? Record your results. Make a sunset by taking a flashlight and shining it lower and lower (like the setting sun). What colors appear in order? Record your results. Pour out half of the solution and shine the flashlight down from the top of the container. Look at bottom. What color is the "sky"? Record your results.

Ϋ How can you prove the earth is round? Devise an experiment.

ϒ Demonstrate weightlessness in space. As an object in orbit falls toward the Earth at the same speed, it travels quickly sideways following a curved orbit, so it misses the Earth's surface. The object is in a "free fall". Make a space capsule to demonstrate this concept. Use a clear plastic bottle (two liter) with a cap. Cut a rubber band and screw the cap of the bottle over the rubber band so that it hangs into the bottle. Take the rubber band out and place a small amount of play dough or putty at one end. Put the putty end into the bottle and *observe* the rubber band. Screw the cap on over the rubber band. Hold the bottle from a distance of one yard (stand on a chair) and drop the bottle. What happens to the rubber band as the bottle drops? How is this similar to what happens to the astronauts? *(How the Universe Works)*.

ϒ Over a one month period record the phases of the moon. Start at the beginning of the month. Plot the changes on a large piece of poster board. Draw out the phases of the moon (or cut out of construction paper). Variation: Make a moon map. Observe the moon using binoculars or a telescope. Try to spot lunar craters, "seas", and other features.

ϒ Observe the constellations. What constellations can you see using a star chart? How do these compare to the star chart of the Gospel message in the stars? Draw a comparison chart of constellations.

ϒ Do an experiment using infrared light. Use two or three mirrors to reflect light. With your parent's permission, try to turn on the television using a remote control pointed away from the set, and mirrors. Does this work? How many mirrors can you use and still have this work?

ϒ Variation: Try the above experiment using a piece of white paper instead of a mirror. Try again using black paper. What happens?

ϒ Make your own compass. (*Bill Nye The Science Guy's Big Blast of Science*)

ϒ What are the different types of stars? Chart the different types of stars and information about each one. Illustrate your findings.

ϒ Demonstrate a pulsar. Tie a long string to a flashlight so that it hangs securely in a horizontal position. Hang from a tree branch and twist the flashlight twenty or thirty times. Turn the flashlight on and let go. What happens? How is this similar to what scientists think about the signals sent by pulsars?

ϒ Create your own "Big Bang". Use a paper bag and fill with ten to twenty popsicle sticks. Inflate the bag and pop it. Do the sticks form any distinct pattern or design? How do you get order from chaos?

Geography and History Ideas
4-8

Ƴ Study astronomers and other early scientists. Choose one astronomer and learn as much as possible about him. Pretend you are his apprentice. What did you find or discover? What was it like living in the ____ century? What was the favorite food, activity, or musician of the day?

Ƴ Map out the places where the scientists lived. Where was the most concentrated number of scientists found? Why?

Ƴ What obstacles did early scientists encounter? Were people willing to believe all of their claims? Why or why not? How were some of these scientists paid to continue their research?

Ƴ Find the southern and northern hemispheres on a globe. List the countries that are found in each of the hemispheres. Make a chart of the constellations that can be seen from the northern hemisphere and a chart of the constellations that can be seen from the southern hemisphere. Compare the two charts. Does one hemisphere see more constellations than the other? What unique feature is in both hemispheres? (Cross constellations are found in both, the Swan [Cygnus] in the north, and the Southern Cross [Crux] in the south!)

ϒ What were the various space exploration vehicles? When did the first space mission take place? What was happening during that time in history? Who were the Presidents during the space missions? Which president has had the most space missions take place during his administration?

ϒ How did early explorers such as Christopher Columbus use their knowledge of the skies to help them in navigation? Did other explorers also make use of the skies? In what ways?

ϒ Locate the Space Center where the astronauts train and the space missions launch, and the alternate landing site.

Art and Music Ideas
4-8

Art

ϒ Make words in the shape of the object they are describing. For example, use the word star and draw the letters in a star shape.

ϒ Make a constellation shirt! Tie dye a shirt blue. Use a plain white tee shirt. Pre-wash the shirt. Tie the shirt in various spots using rubber bands. Twist the fabric, and then put rubber bands in spaces one to two inches apart. Make sure the rubber bands are on tightly. Dip the entire shirt in fabric dye. Follow the directions on the package. Usually the longer you leave the shirt in the dye, the brighter the color. (This is a great project to do outdoors!) You can rinse the shirt immediately, and hang to dry, or place it in a plastic bag for a day or two to allow the colors to set and become brighter. Remove from the dye or plastic bag and rinse under water until the water is almost clear. Remove the rubber bands and rinse a few more times. Wash the shirt in hot water and soap. Let it sit for five to ten minutes. Rinse and lay flat to dry. Paint a constellation on top of your tie-dyed shirt with fabric paints once it is dry. Choose a constellation with a Biblical point (see Teaching Outline). This is a good "conversation" starter.

ϒ Make a "stained-glass" picture of a constellation or the solar system. You will need different colors of tissue paper, glue, a paint brush and heavy background (such as poster board) using various colors of blue, and black. Tear small (1 in.) to medium (2 in.) pieces of tissue paper.

Pour a small pool of glue mixed with several drops of water (to make it spreadable) in a container. Use this mixture with a paint brush to apply the tissue paper onto the poster board. Once this background has dried, use fluorescent paint (or fluorescent glue) to paint a constellation or the solar system. This makes a wonderful wall decoration!

ϒ Make a "stained-glass" design that you can hang. Use heavy black paper, various colors of tissue paper, glue and a sharp knife (X-acto knife works well). Draw a geometric design with 1/2 inch wide lines (spiral from a galaxy, constellation, etc.) Transfer the design to the black paper and carefully cut out with the knife. Glue pieces of tissue paper on the back of the design. Hang when dry!

Music

ϒ William Herschel was a German musician in 1781. What were his contributions? Was he noted for his contributions in music or science?

ϒ Listen to soundtracks from "space" movies (with parental approval). What instruments are used to make the various sounds?

ϒ Begin in the 1600's and make a time line of composers that lived during the days of the early astronomers. Who was the most notable?

Creation Astronomy
Grades 9-12

Objective: To study astronomy from a Biblical perspective through observation, comparison, research, and experiments

Topics of Study: Genesis vs. Big Bang Theory, early astronomers, lightyears, our solar system, stars, constellations and the Gospel message in the stars.

I. The Scientific Study of Astronomy
    A. The Ancient Astronomers
        1. The Greeks
        2. Nicholas Copernicus
        3. Tycho Brahe
        4. Johannes Kepler
        5. Galileo Galilei
        6. Isaac Newton
    B. The Big Bang Theory
        1. An Explanation
        2. Some History
    C. Problems for the Big Bang Theory
        1. Galaxy Clusters
        2. Spiral Arms
        3. Comets
        4. Accretion Disks
        5. Lumpy Rings
        6. Warm Planets
        7. Venus
        8. The Sun
        9. The Moon
        10. The Trapezium of Orion
    D. The Speed of Light
        1. The Speed of Light Today
        2. The Speed of Light and the Six Days of Creation
        3. Evolutionists Address Their Problems
    E. The Solar System
        1. Sun, Moon
        2. Earth and Planets

II. The Biblical Study of Astronomy
    A. The Heavens Declare the Glory
        1. The Milky Way

    2. Radio-Astronomers
    3. Observing the Stars
B. The Gospel Message in the Stars
    1. Virgo
        a. Coma
        b. Centaurus
        c. Bootes
    2. Libra
        a. Crux
        b. Victima
        c. Corona
    3. Scorpio
        a. Serpens
        b. Ophiuchus
        c. Hercules
    4. Sagittarius
        a. Lyra
        b. Ara
        c. Draco
    5. Capricornus
        a. Sagitta
        b. Aquila
        c. Delphinus
    6. Aquarius
        a. Pisces Australis
        b. Pegasus
        c. Sygnus
    7. Pisces
        a. The Band
        b. Cephus
        c. Andromeda
    8. Aries
        a. Cassiopeia
        b. Cetus
        c. Perseus
    9. Taurus
        a. Orion
        b. Eridanus
        c. Auriga
    10. Gemini
        a. Lepus
        b. Canis Major
        c. Canis Minor
    11. Cancer
        a. Ursa Minor
        b. Ursa Major
        c. Argo
    12. Leo
        a. Hydra
        b. Crater
        c. Corvus

Lesson Plans

Ancient Astronomers

Subject	Monday	Tuesday	Wednesday	Thursday	Friday
Bible/Religion Studies	TS				
Astronomy Teaching Outline Ancient Astronomers	Ancient Astronomers		Ancient Astronomers	Modern Astronomers	
Reading Selection	TS				
Vocab/Spell/ Grammar Language Arts	Assign 20-30 words from list or reading		Use words in sentences Research Astronomer		Study origins and meanings of vocabulary words
Math Reinforcement		Study Metric system and why it is used		Measure the diameter of the moon	
Science Activities and Experiments	Observe moon and stars for a month and chart them		Draw the constellations		Which constellation are seen in winter and summer
Geography/History Ideas		Study history of Astronomy		Write biography of different astronomers	
Art/Music		Draw constellations you see in the evening			
Math: TS					
Literature TS					

LA= Language Arts   CR= Creation Resource: Read Selected Books from resource list or others
TS= Teacher Selection   AR= Astronomy Resource: Other books that fit the topic

Lesson Plans

Big Bang Theory

Subject	Monday	Tuesday	Wednesday	Thursday	Friday
Bible/Religion Studies	TS				
Astronomy Teaching Outline Big Bang Theory	Explanation of Big Bang Theory	Some problems with the Big Bang Theory			
Reading Selection	TS				
Vocab/Spell/ Grammar Language Arts	Assign 20-30 words from list or reading		Pre-Test vocabulary words		Open-ended story using vocabulary words
Math Reinforcement		Study Bode's Law and the number system			
Science Activities and Experiments	Build a rocket froma kit or scratch		What is the brightness scale of the stars?		Chart brightest stars, nearest, double, variable, clusters, nebulae, etc.
Geography/History Ideas		Map where astronomers lived		TS	
Art/Music		Do color-resist watercolor painting of a constellation		TS	
Math: TS					
Literature					

LA= Language Arts
TS= Teacher Selection

CR= Creation Resource: Read Selected Books from resource list or others
AR= Astronomy Resource: Other books that fit the topic

Lesson Plans

<table>
<tr><td>Big Bang Theory and its Problems</td></tr>
</table>

Subject	Monday	Tuesday	Wednesday	Thursday	Friday
Bible/Religion Studies	TS				
Astronomy Teaching Outline Problems and Speed of Light	Explain some problems with the Big Bang Theory		Discuss speed of light today and at Creation		
Reading Selection		TS		TS	
Vocab/Spell/ Grammar Language Arts	Assign word form list or reading		Tape and 'interview' with a famous astronomer		Study Scriptures that refer to con-stellations
Math Reinforcement		Calculate distances in AU			
Science Activities and Experiments	Discuss brightness scale, observe and make chart		Create your own Big Bang Observe results		TS
Geography/History Ideas		Compare observations of the universe through the centuries			
Art/Music		Make marbled paper to resemble the surface of some planets			
Math: TS					
Literature					

LA= Language Arts   CR= Creation Resource: Read Selected Books from resource list or others
TS= Teacher Selection   AR= Astronomy Resource: Other books that fit the topic

Lesson Plans

	Solar System				

Subject	Monday	Tuesday	Wednesday	Thursday	Friday
Bible/Religion Studies	TS				
Astronomy Teaching Outline Solar System	Planetary Astronomy Solar System				
Reading Selection	TS				
Vocab/Spell/ Grammar Language Arts	Big Bang Creation vs. Evolution debate		Write newsletter for astronomers		Write letter to the editor relating to Big Bang
Math Reinforcement		Compare word equations with symbolic ones			
Science Activities and Experiments	Build your own telescope				Photograph stars with long exposure
Geography/History Ideas		First man in space, first astronaut, other first		Neil Armstrong on the moon	
Art/Music		Listen to Jupiter Symphony by Mozart		Art: TS	
Math: TS					
Literature					

LA= Language Arts   CR= Creation Resource: Read Selected Books from resource list or others
TS= Teacher Selection   AR= Astronomy Resource: Other books that fit the topic

Lesson Plans

Gospel Message In The Stars

Subject	Monday	Tuesday	Wednesday	Thursday	Friday
Bible/Religion Studies	TS				
Astronomy Teaching Outline Gospel in the Stars	Milky Way		Radio Astronomy		TS
Reading Selection	TS				
Vocab/Spell/ Grammar Language Arts	Test		Do a Creation Astronomy presentation		TS
Math Reinforcement		Chart of comparison of planets to earth			
Science Activities and Experiments	Demonstrate effect of meteors and meteorites		Study names of stars in the constellations and their meanings		
Geography/History Ideas		Research the Mir Space Station			
Art/Music		Compose your own song about the Gospel Message in Stars			
Math: TS					
Literature					

LA= Language Arts   CR= Creation Resource: Read Selected Books from resource list or others
TS= Teacher Selection   AR= Astronomy Resource: Other books that fit the topic

Lesson Plans

Gospel Message In The Stars

Subject	Monday	Tuesday	Wednesday	Thursday	Friday
Bible/Religion Studies	TS				
Astronomy Teaching Outline Gospel in the Stars	Gospel Message in the Stars				
Reading Selection	TS				
Vocab/Spell/ Grammar Language Arts	Test of terms		Write poem about one of the constellations		How many "space" names can you find in daily life
Math Reinforcement		Make a sky clock			
Science Activities and Experiments	Demonstrate and measure centripetal force		Study Viking, Magellan and Voyager space probes		Build a model of the solar system
Geography/History Ideas		Research some of the tragedies in the space program			
Art/Music		Study classical music from the 17th –19th centuries			
Math: TS					
Literature					

LA= Language Arts CR= Creation Resource: Read Selected Books from resource list or others
TS= Teacher Selection AR= Astronomy Resource: Other books that fit the topic

Reading
Activity and Experiment
Resource List 9-12

Reading: *Books contain a Christian content and may be difficult to find in the library.

Astronomy and the Bible Questions and Answers by Donald B. DeYoung
> Baker Book House: 1993, 146 pp. Astronomy written from a Creation perspective! This book is very informative and contains information about the solar system, stars, galaxies, universe, technical terms and ideas.

Isaac Newton: Mastermind of Modern Science, by David C. Knight.
> Publisher: Franklin Watts, 1961, 55 pp. Isaac Newton contributed much to science, not only in the discovery of gravity. This book is about his life and his contributions.

Starlight and Time Solving the Puzzle of Distant Starlilght in a Young Universe by D. Russell
> Humphreys, Ph. D. Master Books: 1994, 137 pp. Creation scientists have a new answer to the question of stars that appear to be billions of light years away in a young universe .

Turn Left At Orion, by Guy Consolmagno and Dan M. Davis
> Publisher: Cambridge University Press, 1989, 205 pp. Contains detailed information about what can be viewed in the night sky. The book is illustrated as if you are looking through a telescope lens. The details and accompanying information will demonstrate the modern trend of labeling stars with letters and numbers rather than names.

Voyage to the Stars, by Richard Bliss
> Publisher: Institute of Creation Research, 1991, 111 pp. This book is written by a Creation Scientist with an emphasis on the study of the stars and telescopes, using a fictitious space mission featuring student astronauts. This book effectively presents difficult material in an interesting way.

Activity and Experiments Books:

Astronomy and the Bible by Donald B. DeYoung
> Baker Books: 1989, 146 pp. An excellent enrichment divided into six sections astronomy!

Astronomy for Every Kid 101 by Janice VanCleave
> John Wiley & Sons, Inc., 1991, 230 pp. Great experiments that demonstrate many of the concepts discussed in this study.

Bill Nye The Science Guy's Big Blast of Science, by Bill Nye
> Addison-Wesley: 1993, 172 pp. (See additional review under 4-8)

Design and Origins in Astronomy , by George Mulfinger, ed.
> Creation Research Society: 1983, 152 pp. This book is for the serious science student. It is difficult reading, yet contains many informative articles about astronomy from a Creation viewpoint.

Projects in Space Science, by Robert Gardner
> Julian Messner, 1988, 128 pp. This is an excellent book containing scientific activities and experiments that deal with all of the major aspects of space science.

Telescope Power, by Gregory Matloff
> Publisher: John Wiley & Sons, 1993, 119 pp. This book has easy-to-understand information about using telescopes, defining different kinds, what to look for and how to get started in astronomy.

Unlocking the Mysteries of Creation by Dennis Peterson
> Master Books, 2002, 240 pp. see review under 4-8)

Vocabulary/Spelling List

9-12

These words are to be used as a base for your vocabulary and spelling list. If the words are unknown, have the child research them either in a dictionary, science dictionary, or encyclopedia.

aberration, optical

absolute magnitude

absolute zero

absorption spectra

Andromeda galaxy

apparent magnitude

asterism

astrophysics

bright light spectra

calcium

Cassegrain telescope

catadioptic telescope

celestial equator

cepheid variable

circumpolar

constellation

classical cepheids

clock drive

dark line spectra

diffraction grating

electromagnetic

radiation/spectrum

escape velocity

extrapolate

Greek alphabet

gyrocompass

helium

Horsehead Nebula

Hubble space

telescope

hydrogen

hyperbolic

infrared radiation

ionosphere

Kelvin

luminosity

main sequence star

mare

Messier numbers

military clock

nadir

neutron star

nova star

optical sensors

parsec

penumbra

perigee

photon

photosphere

Pogson scale

proper motion

radiation

rectangular coordinates

relative motion

relative position

right ascension

scattering

Schmidt telescope

setting circles

solar prominences

spectroanalysis

spectra

spectral lines

spectrograph

terminator

thermonuclear reaction

transit

troposphere

Van Allen Radiation

Belt

variable star

Vocabulary/ Spelling and Grammar Ideas
9-12

ϒ Use the vocabulary and spelling words interchangeably in the following activities.

ϒ A pre-test of spelling and vocabulary is a good indication of the words children already know. Dictate the words orally, or by audio cassette, and let them spell the words and write a brief definition.

ϒ Have children look up the words (that they do not know) in a dictionary, science dictionary or encyclopedia and write the words and a brief definition of each. Then have them write the words in complete sentences using as many parts of speech as they can think of. Have them use a thesaurus.

ϒ Use the sentences to label and diagram the parts of speech. Refer to a language book, if necessary.

ϒ Test to see that they know the definitions of the vocabulary words. Use different formats: oral test, multiple choice, true or false, etc.

ϒ Study the origins of the vocabulary words. What languages do they originate from? Were their original meanings the same as their meanings today? (You may not be able to find this information in a standard dictionary. Try the Internet using online dictionaries or encyclopedias.)

ϒ Have your children make up original crossword puzzles. Try to use words that are difficult to remember. Use around ten to twelve words for each puzzle. They can give these to adults to work out, then check the answers! Have older children make puzzles for younger children (using age appropriate vocabulary words).

ϒ Use the vocabulary words for a word search puzzle. Make it more difficult by putting words in backwards and diagonally.

ϒ Make a "space" game. Use construction paper and grid the board. Put in obstacles like "Black Hole: lose a turn", etc. Place the vocabulary words on the spaces and number them. Give each word (depending on its difficulty) a number of spaces you can move. For example, if you land on the space containing the word "calcium" and correctly define the word, you can move two spaces. If the word was "relative motion" and it was correctly defined, you might move five spaces. Make up vocabulary answer sheets corresponding to the numbered vocabulary words on the board for an easy reference. This is a great way to learn difficult words.

Language Arts Ideas
9-12

ϒ Research different astronomers. Pick an astronomer of interest. Write a biographical sketch of this person's life. What type of education was necessary for his degree?   How many years of school, etc.? What was sacrificed (family, time, religion) in the quest for knowledge?

ϒ Do the same activity as an autobiography. Another variation is to add fictionalized accounts.

ϒ Write poetry, using different styles, about one of the constellations using the Gospel message in the stars approach.

ϒ Use a paragraph from a book you are reading for dictation. Check for proper spelling, punctuation, and form.

ϒ Research current day astronomers in the space industry (NASA). What type of education is necessary? What is the advantage/ disadvantage of working with large industry?

ϒ What is a junior astronomer? What type of equipment is necessary? What types of careers are available to someone who decides to go into the field of astronomy?

ϒ Research astronomers who have made major discoveries. (For example: Halley) What would happen if the astronomer made an error? (Tycho Brache believed a strange theory of planetary motion which was later disproved.) Make a tape recording of an "interview" with an astronomer who is about to make a major discovery. Have your questions prepared before you do this activity. Perhaps have someone interview you!

ϒ Study the constellations. Learn about what they tell us about the Gospels. Teach someone else about the original meanings of the star names.

ϒ Is there life on other planets or in other solar systems? Why or why not? Do an oral presentation of your view. Be prepared to answer questions from the audience.

ϒ Write a story about a person (prophet) from the Old Testament who might have observed the constellations in the sky and told about the coming of a Messiah.

ϒ Write a newsletter for astronomers. "_____ First to report ground breaking information. Hubble telescope reveals the stars are younger than once believed!" Or how about: "New (name of your device) improves the clarity of earth telescopes without the cost of sending telescopes into space!"   Put in advertisements for different tools of the trade, equipment such as telescopes and parts, as well as observation towers or planetariums (where there is research going on). Include articles from all "types" of scientists.

ϒ Stage a "Creation vs. Evolution" debate. Be prepared to explain the problems with the big bang and discoveries scientists have made without any explanation or data to back up their claims (see teaching outline for information).

ϒ Do a "Creation Astronomy" presentation. Make star charts using the constellation explanations given for the Gospel message in the stars (see teaching outline).

ϒ Play charades. Each person "acts out" a constellation using its true meaning. The other team (or person) guesses what constellation is being enacted.

ϒ See how many "space" names you can find which are used by the automotive industry. For example: Mercury, Comet, AeroStar, Subaru (whose symbol means constellation), etc.

ϒ Study the Greek and Latin origin of words. *(English from the Roots Up)*

Math Reinforcement Ideas
9-12

ϒ Learn about the metric system. Why is this used in scientific experimentation?

ϒ Make a chart of metric equivalents, using inches, feet, yards, and miles converted to centimeters, meters, and kilometers. Also convert cups and gallons to liters and milliliters. Change ounces and pounds to grams and kilograms.

ϒ What is the difference between a word equation and a symbol equation? How are these used in scientific experimentation?

ϒ Study the angles of light which hit the earth and affect the season's temperature. (See Science experiment section) What geometric angles are used? What are the degrees of the angles?

ϒ Measure the sun's diameter. (**Never look directly in the sun)** Tape two pieces of white poster board to two ends of a yardstick. Poke a small pin hole in the card on the top of the yardstick. Light rays from the sun will pass through the pinhole and make an image of the sun on the card at the bottom. Measure this image. Make a ratio of the diameter of this image to the length of the yardstick and the diameter of the sun to 93,000,000 miles. *(Projects in Space Science)*

ϒ Measure the diameter of the moon. Make a square hole in an index card, 1/2 in. on each side. When the moon is directly overhead, lie on the ground and have someone move the square until you see the moon fill up the square. Measure the distance from your eye to the square and calculate the distance to the moon. Remember: Ratio d/h = the ratio D/H (little d = the distance from your eye to the square, h is the size of the square, D = the distance to the moon which is 240,000 miles and H is the diameter of the moon)

ϒ Study Bode's Law (He was an astronomer from the 1700's). A number scheme was developed. How was this number system used by astronomers? (AU: astronomical units) (*Projects in Space Science*).

ϒ Calculate the distance to Neptune and Pluto in AU (astronomical units).

ϒ Make a sky clock. Use precise measurements. You will be able to tell time on a clear night! As the Earth turns every twenty-four hours, the stars seem to move around the North Star (or Polaris). If adjusted to the right date and pointed at Polaris, you can tell the correct time. You will need a protractor for this activity. *(How the Universe Works)*

ϒ Make an accelerometer. This is a device that allows you to detect acceleration. (*Projects in Space Science*)

ϒ Make a device to measure centripetal forces. See how mass, radius and period are related to the centripetal force needed to keep a satellite in orbit.*(Projects in Space Science)*

ϒ What is a light-year? How do scientists estimate how many light years away the nearest visible stars are to Earth? What mathematical equation can you write to prove this?

ϒ Write light speed in miles per second, kilometers per second, miles per hour, kilometers per hour. Make a chart with your results. How long does it take for light to travel around the Earth at the equator? (*Bill Nye The Science Guy's Big Blast of Science*)

ϒ Make a chart of all the planets comparing diameter, mass, density, time to orbit the sun, radius of orbit. Give Earth a constant of 1.0 for all categories except mass (5.5). (*Projects in Space Science*)

ϒ Study Einstein's formula $E=mc^2$ What does the c stand for? What do Creation Scientists believe about the speed of light?

ϒ Variation: How does Einstein's formula relate to the first Law of Thermodynamics?

Science Activities and Experiments
9-12

Remember to never, never look at the sun! See introduction page vi for scientific method information and page 167 for scientific method copy sheets.

Υ Discover the properties of gravity. Drop a ball several times from different heights (one foot, one yard, two yards, from a balcony, etc.) Measure the time by counting (or using a stopwatch). Does the ball fall at a steady speed under the force of gravity? Does it accelerate?

Υ When observing the stars in the evening you should cover your flashlight with red cellophane or paint the lens with red nail polish. Why is this important? What effect does the white light have on your eyes and your viewing of objects in the dark? (Why is red light used at night in submarines?)

Υ Variation: Devise an experiment using a flashlight without a red cellophane covered lens, and one with. Use your family (or other willing volunteers) and survey the difference in what they can see using the different lights.

Υ Make a rocket! There are many good rocket kits in science magazines, nature stores, and toy stores. Better yet, research, design and build your own! Find out who first invented rockets, and what war rocket was developed into the Saturn V moon-launcher. What was the first re-usable space vehicle? What is an impulse engine?

ϒ Find out what space experiments were done on space missions to determine the effects of zero gravity.

ϒ Design and build your own telescope! See the resource section for addresses to write to for more information.

ϒ Demonstrate an ellipse. Tack a piece of paper to a cork board (or some similar surface). Tie a piece of string into a loop. Stick a tack into the center of the paper with the string attached. Put a pencil into the loop and pull the string taut. Move the pencil around the tack. What shape did you draw? Put another tack into the paper three cm. away from the other one. Put the string around both tacks. Put the pencil in the loop, pull taut and move the pencil around the tacks. What shape did you draw? The shape drawn with a set loop of string around two points is an ellipse. Continue to move the tack (not the center tack). What shape do you get? What scientist discovered that planets travel in ellipses around the sun? (*Bill Nye The Science Guy's Big Blast of Science*)

ϒ Using various objects and a large flashlight, try to find an object that always casts a round shadow. Use the scientific method. What did early astronomers think about the earth, moon and sun?

ϒ What patterns can you find in the night sky? Draw the constellations you observe. Compare your findings to a star chart.

♈ What constellations can be seen prominently in the winter months? In the summer months?

♈ What is the brightness scale of stars? How many stars can you observe? Make a chart of the stars in Orion. Label the different stars.

♈ What star events take place at different times of the year? For example in July or August the second brightest star in Lyra, "Beta Lyrae" which is a binary star (one of two stars) sometimes passes in front of the other to form eclipsing binaries! *(Telescope Power)*

♈ Try photographing the stars. You will need a camera that allows the shutter to remain open for a long exposure. Mount a camera on a tripod or other firm surface. Point the camera to the brightest stars and leave the shutter open for one minute or more (according to the film speed). What did your photographs show? (The color film should show the colors of the stars more clearly than you can see them with your eyes!) Do this over a series of several nights. Chart your results.

♈ Track the nearest planets. Find Mercury, Venus, Mars, Jupiter and Saturn. Find a good star chart book, and it will have the dates the planets are thought to be visible. (Isn't it amazing how orderly our universe is and that this can be predicted years ahead of time?)

♈ Planets do not shine with their own light like the stars do. Why not?

What information can you find to substantiate your claim? Can you set up a demonstration of this with a 3-D model?

ϒ Never look directly at the sun!! What famous astronomer observed the sun and permanently damaged his eyes? Observe the sun by catching sun rays in a pair of binoculars (cap one of the lenses with a piece of cardboard taped to the end) and project the sun onto another sheet of paper, such as a piece of cardboard. You can move the paper to adjust the focus of the image until it is as sharp or as big as you would like it to be. Draw the shape of the sun. Draw any sunspots, solar flares or other things that show up. *(Usborne Guide The Young Astronomer)*

ϒ Make a chart using the following headings: the brightest stars, nearest stars, double stars, variable stars, star clusters, nebulae, and galaxies. Write down the constellation where it was found, magnitude of the star, and distance from the earth. Why are so many stars and constellations now given numbers instead of names? Why do you think these are different from the original names of the constellations?

ϒ Demonstrate the effects of meteors and meteorites hitting the Earth. Use various techniques to do this. For example, use sand and a large heavy object, such as a baseball. Throw the ball towards the sand as you can. you can. What happened? What are the effects of meteors on the Earth? What does the fossil record show about meteors?

ϒ Observe Mars. It is thought that iron compounds on the soil of Mars make it appear red. Try this: take a baking dish and put a layer of sand on the bottom. Cut some steel wool into two cm. pieces, and mix into the sand. Pour enough water in to cover the sand. Leave for several days. Add water as needed to keep the mixture moist. Each day check your results. What happened? How many days did it take before the mixture appeared to be the same color as the planet Mars?

ϒ Create your own "big bang". Take a balloon and fill with ¼ cup of confetti. Inflate the balloon and pop it. Does the confetti make a distinct pattern or design? How do you get order from chaos?

ϒ The Viking landers made tests on Martian soil hoping to find microscopic life. They only found chemically reactive soil. Duplicate the tests made by a space probe. Fill three jars ½ full of sand.   Label each jar.   Mix two tsp. salt in one jar, two tsp. baking powder in one jar, and two tsp. yeast in one. Place in the refrigerator overnight (Mars is cold!).   The next day pour equal amounts of water in each jar. What happened? Which jar contains "life"? *(How the Universe Works)* What happened? What are the effects of meteors on the Earth? What does the fossil record show about meteors?

Geography and History Ideas
9-12

ϒ Study the history of astronomy. Note the different beliefs through the ages. When did their (scientists) beliefs begin to change? What was happening in the world? How did the scientific beliefs change the thinking at the time? Compare the seventeenth through twentieth centuries.

ϒ Study and read about different astronomers and scientists throughout history. Write a biographical sketch.

ϒ Map where the astronomers lived. What do you notice about where they lived? Did the geographical location affect their discoveries?

ϒ Compare the early findings about the origins of the universe through the centuries. Use a chart and list the changes in belief as they began to be stated publicly. What was happening in history during this time?

ϒ Find out who was the first man in space and the name of his spacecraft. Who was the first American astronaut and the name of his spacecraft? List subsequent space flights and the astronauts involved. Variation: Was man the first to fly in space?

ϒ Where did the astronauts launch and land? How did their missions change though the years?

ϒ When was the Russian Mir Space Station built? How long has it been in orbit?

ϒ When did Neil Armstrong first step on the moon? What was his famous quote? What were the historical conditions of the day?

ϒ Why was the first space shuttle named *Enterprise*?

ϒ What were some of the tragedies of the space program through time? What was learned from the mistakes made?

ϒ What space technology has been incorporated into everyday life? Make a list and add to it! (For example: Tang, velcro, etc.)

Art and Music Ideas
9-12

Art

ϒ Make a star chart. Draw constellations and label them.

ϒ Make a scrapbook of different constellations you have seen (on evening field trips or nature walks). Label, date, and tell the location of where they were found.

ϒ Do a "crayon-resist" watercolor painting. Draw a scene with different constellations in the night sky during a particular season. Color the scene lightly with crayon. Take water colors and paint over the crayon drawing with a light wash (little color on the paint brush). Use different colors. What is the effect? What happens where there is crayon? Why?

ϒ Make marbled paper. (This looks like some of the surfaces of the planets. Which ones?) Use medium-weight paper, oil and food coloring. In a glass cup mix several drops (four to five) of each food color with ½ teaspoon of oil. Mix as many of each color as you wish to use. Place water in a dishpan at least three inches deep. Sprinkle small drops of colored oil into the water. Swirl with a toothpick or straw, but don't over-mix! Carefully lay the paper on the water. Let it lie flat, then lift it out. Dry the paper flat. This makes a great book cover!

Music

ϒ Make a study of classical music from the seventeenth (or earlier), eighteenth, nineteenth and twentieth centuries. What astronomers lived during each period of time? (Make a time line of composers and astronomer/scientists of the day.) What changes in the musical form can be found during these periods of time? Who were the people who often commissioned the composers to write their music? How has this changed today?

ϒ Listen to the "Jupiter Symphony" by Mozart! When and why did he write this?

ϒ Compose your own song about the constellations. Use a popular melody from a song you enjoy. Write original words using one or two of the constellations from the Gospel message in the stars! Record your song!

Resource Books/Videos
and Computer and Internet
All Ages

Here are some *suggested* resources for doing this unit. Some of these books have a Christian content and are marked with an *. These may be purchased from the Creation science sources listed on page 114.

Adventures in the Solar System Planetron and Me Williams and Regan, Price/Stern/Sloan Publishers, Inc., 1987. (K-8)

Amazing Space Facts Dinah L. Moche, Golden Book, 1988. (K-6)

Astronauts Dinah Moche, Random House, 1978. (K-6)

Astronomy for Every Kid Janice VanCleave, John Wiley & Sons, Inc., 1991. (K-8)

*Astronomy and the Bible, Donald B. DeYoung, Baker Books, 1989. (4-12)

Astronomy Adventures NatureScope, National Wildlife Federation, 1989. (K-8)

Big Book of Space Robin Kerrod, Gallery Books, 1988. (K-6)

Bill Nye The Science Guy's® Big Blast of Science Bill Nye, Wesley Publishing, 1993. (6-12)

Bubbles Rainbows and Worms Sam Ed. Brown, Gryphon House, Inc., 1981. (Pre-K- 1)

Exploring Your Solar System National Geographic Society, 1989. (K-12)

Facts and Lists Usborne, EDC Publishing, 1989. (K-12)

Find the Constellations H.A. Rey, Houghton Mifflin, 1988. (4-8)

Flight (Sticker Book) Stewart and Stewart III, Harper & Row, 1987. (K-6)

How the Universe Works Couper/ Henbest, Reader's Digest, 1994. (K-12)

If You Were An Astronaut Dinah Moche, Western Publishing, 1985. (K-6)

The Kid's NatureBook 365 Indoor/Outdoor Activities and Experiences Susan Milford, Williamson *Publishing, 1989. (K-8)*

* Men of Science Men of God Morris , Master Books, 1993. (4-12)

My First Book About Space A Question and Answer Book Dinah Moche, Western Publishing, 1985. (K-3)

Outdoor Science Projects For Young People George Barr, General Publishing Co., 1959. (K-12)

Projects in Space Science Robert Gardner, Julian Messner Publishing, 1988. (K-12)

Rockets and Satellites Franklyn Branley, Harper & Row, 1987. (K-3)

* Science and the Bible Donald DeYoung, Baker Books, 1994. (K-6)

Science Toolbox Making and Using the Tools of Science Jean Stangl,
Tab Books, 1994. K-8

Space Scientist Telescopes and Observatories Couper and Henbest, Franklyn Watts, 1987. (4-8)

Space Sticker Book Robin Kerrod, Chatham River Press, 1988 . (K-6)

Space Telescope A New True Book Dennis Fradin, Children's Chicago Press, 1987. (K-3)

Spotter's Guide to the Night Sky Usborne EDC Publications, 1979. (K-12)

Star Guide A Voyage Into Space Franklyn Branley, Thomas Y. Crowell Publishing, 1987. (K-8)

Stars A Golden Guide Zim and Baker, Golden Press, 1975. (K-12)

Stars Seymour Simon, William Morrow & Co., 1986. (K-6)

* Streams of Civilization Volume One Hyma and Stanton, Creation-Life Publishers, 1992. (K-12)

Sun, Moon and Planets Myring and Snowden, EDC Publishing, Usborne, 1982.(K-6)

The Astronomy Book Dr. Jonathan Henry, Master Books, 1999, (2-12)

The Sun Our Nearest Star Franklyn Branley, Harper & Row, 1988. (K-3)

Telescope Power Fantastic Activities and Easy Projects for Young Astronomers Gregory Matloff, John Wiley & Sons, 1993. (4-12)

Turn Left At Orion Consolmagno and Davis, Cambridge University Press, 1989. (6-12)

*Unlocking the Mysteries of Creation Dennis Peterson, Creation Resource Foundation, 1986. (K-12)

The Usborne Dictionary of Science Physics, Chemistry & Biology Facts Usborne, EDC Publishing, 1988. (7-12)

Unlocking the Mysteries of Creation Dennis Peterson, Master Books, 2002. (K-12)

What Is A Star? Arvetis and Palmer, Field Publications, 1988. (Pre K-3)

Young Astronomer Sheila Snowden, Usborne EDC Publishing, 1989. (K-8)

Star Charts
Luminous Star Finder Hubbard Scientific Company (can be purchased from Nasco or Delta Science Catalogs)
Star Theater Halogen Planetarium Projector with one hour audio tape and activity guide. (may be purchased from Nasco or Delta)

Videos:
Tell Me Why Space, Earth, and Atmosphere Volume 1 Prism Entertain. (K-12) Our family's favorite series of educational videos. Informative, and best of all, the children remember the information! (Delta Education)

Audio Cassettes
Wee Sing Around the World Geography Songs Audio Memory (K-12)
Wee Sing Around the Campfire (K-12)

Computer Software:
Astronomer CD-ROM Expert Software (6-12)
Multimedia planetarium program with historic videos, computer simulations, narration and sound!

Internet:
There are lots of interesting resources available via the Internet on the topic of astronomy. I have links on my website www.MediaAngels.com Here are some keywords you may want to try: space, astronomy, stellar astronomy, planets, NASA, space station, stars, etc.

Media Angels web site: http:\\www.MediaAngels.com
We have many Creation science links, free experiments of the month to download and a listing of some of our favorite home school sites.

Games:
Scientists Card Game Aristoplay (1-12)

Other Books of Interest that help with unit studies

A Taste of the Classics Patrick Kavanaugh, Sparrow Press,1993
Elements of Style by Strunk/White (Good reference book!)(6-12)
Children's World Atlas Rand McNally, 1989. (4-12)
English from the Roots Up Volume I Lundquist (4-12)
If You're Trying to Teach Kids How to Write You've Gotta Have This Book! Marjorie Frank, (K-6) Great book with lots of good ideas. Highly recommended by one of the editors of this book, Chris Thomas!
Let the Author's Speak Carolyn Hatcher, 1992, Old Pinnacle Pub.
Story of Music Usborne (K-12), EDC Publishing History of music!

Space/Science Resources

Write to the following places for more information.

Spacecraft and Airplane Models	
Acme Rocket Company www.acmerocket.com	Box 28283 Tempe, AZ 85285
Flight Systems, Inc.	9300 East 68th Street Raytown, MO 64233
Toys and Models Corporation	222 River Street Hackensack, NJ 07601
Scale Models, Inc.	111 Independence Drive Menlo Park, CA 94025
Souvenirs and Memorabilia of Space	
AW/JSC Exchange Store www.JCS.NASA.gov. www.spacecenter.org	Johnson Space Center Houston, TX 77058
Spaceport USA Tours www.hobbyspace.com/spaceports	TW Recreational Services, Inc. Kennedy Space Center, FL 32899
Smithsonian Institute www.si.edu.edu www.nasm.si.edu.edu	Museum Shops 900 Jefferson Drive SW Washington, DC 20560
Sky-Lab Foods (Space-Type freeze-dried food) http://spacelink.nasa.gov/instructional.materials/ nasa.educational.products/space.food.and.nutrition/skylab.html	177 Lake Street White Plains, NY 16040
Information	
National Geographic Society www.nationalgeographic.com	Box 2806 Washington, DC 20036
NASA (kits for teachers on Space: send request on letterhead stationary with your school's name) This service is for educators only Request elementary or secondary education. www.nasa.gov	Education Services Branch Mail Code PA-ESB, Kennedy Space Center, FL 32899 407-867-4444
National Technical Information Services (Scientific and technical information) www.ntis.gov www.fedworld.gov	5285 Port Royal Road Springfield, VA 22151

Additional Resources

Institute of Creation Research Dr. John Morris: President	P.O. Box 1606 El Cajon, CA 92022	619-448-0900 800-628-7640 www.ICR.org
Censored Science Catie Frates (homeschool mom/scientist/author/ lecturer)	Great creation resources	www.CatieFrates.com www.MediaAngels.com
Answers in Genesis Ken Ham	P.O. Box 6330 Florence, KY 41022	800-778-3390 www.AnswersinGenesis.org
Creation Resource Foundation Dennis R. Petersen	P.O. Box 570 El Dorado, CA 95623	530-626-4447 www.creationresource.org
Creation Studies Institute (Creation Science information and resources)	2401 West Cypress Creek Rd. Ft. Lauderdale, FL 33309	800-882-0278 www.creationstudies.org
Delta Education (lots of science materials K-8)	P.O. Box 950 Hudson, NH 030501	800-442-5444 www.delta-education.com
Nasco Science (all types of science materials and equipment for K-12)	901 Janesvillle Ave. Ft. Atkinson, WI 53538-0901	800-558-9595 www.eNasco.com
Educational Resources (Computer Programs)	1550 Executive Drive Elgin, Illinois 60123	800-624-2926 www.edresources.com
God's World Books Educational Catalog	P.O. Box 2330 Asheville, NC 28802	800-951-BOOK www.gwbc.com
Edmund Scientific (Materials and kits for experiments)	60 Pearce Ave. Tonawanda, NY 14150	1-800-728-6999 www.scientificsonline.com
Educational Resources		www.eric.ed.gove
Adorama (send for catalog of telescopes)	42 W. 18th St., New York, NY 10011	1-800-223-2500 www.adorama.com
Lumicon (send for catalog of telescopes)	2111 Research Drive #5 S. Livermore, CA 94500	1-800-767-9576 www.lumicon.com
Astro PTX Astronomy supplies	57 N. Street Suite 401 Danbury, CT 06810	860-355-3132 www.astroptx.com

Scientific, and Government Resources

For most of the places below it would be helpful to write on "school letterhead stationery" when making your request in writing. If you call, you can tell them you are a private school or home school. If letterhead is a must, I have listed it below.

NASA CORE (Central Operation of Resources of Educators) Has slides, videos, and audio tapes. Catalogs are available.	NASA Core Lorain County,Joint Vocational School 15181 Rt. 58 S. Oberlin, OH 44074 www.nasa.gov
National Air and Space Museum's Educational Resource Center (This has aerospace-related public domain software; write for a catalog.)	Office of Education P-700 National Air and Space Museum Washington, D.C. 20560 www.nasm.si.edu
National Geographic Society (Write for educational kits and audiovisuals and satellite maps!) To preview or rent films and videos write : Karol Media 22 Riverview Dr. Wayne, NJ 07470-3191	National Geographic Society Educational Services Dept. 89 Washington, DC 20036 www.nationalgeographic.com
The Universe in the Classroom (for free newsletter on teaching astronomy sponsored by the Astronomical Society of the Pacific and the American Astronomical Society; has short articles, activities and guides. Use "school letterhead" stationary when making request.)	Astronomical Society of the Pacific 390 Ashoton Ave. San Francisco, CA 94122 www.astrosociety.org www.sciencenet.org.uk
Astronomy on a Shoestring (Activity guide on science teacher activities, for 4th grade and up)	National Science Teachers Association 1742 Connecticut Ave. N.W. Washington, DC 20009 www.nsta.org
Astronomy Educational Materials Resources Guide (Lists activities and sources for K-12 for more information or to order)	Astronomy Education Materials Network Dept. of Curriculum and Instruction West Virginia University Morgantown, WV 26506 www.scienceteacher.org
National Audiovisual Center (Has filmstrips, videos, and slides for purchase, preview, or rental. Write for a catalog on "school letterhead".)	National Audiovisual Center 8700 Edgeworth Dr. Capitol Heights, MD 20743 www.ntis.gov/products/types/audiovisual/index.asp

Materials List **Here are some items you may find useful in doing this unit :**

compass
balance scale (science catalogs)
balls (various sizes)
binoculars
brush
Bunsen burner (older grades, order from science catalogs)
containers (various sizes)
dropper
flashlight (with lens covered with red polish or paper)
glass beaker (with metric)
measuring cup (metric)
plaster of Paris
poster board
ruler (with metric)
scissors
star chart
telescope (optional)
test tubes (various sizes, order from science catalogs)
timer

Field Trip Guide

Nature Walk
Nature Center
Nature Supply Stores
Planetarium
Museums (New Creation museums are cropping up all over the USA. Do a keyword search using the words "Creation Museum" online.)

Creation Science Institute Peace River (Arcadia, Florida) Canoe Trip. This is a canoe and camping trip and fossil hunt led by Creation Scientists! A great opportunity to learn about science and great star-gazing! Check CSI's website (www.creationstudies.com) for information about when their trip will take place. Usually scheduled twice a year in the fall and spring.

Another wonderful opportunity for Creation trips is Creation Expeditions! Join the DeRosa family as they visit and host various trips with a Creation focus. Check their website at www.creationexpeditions.com and www.overjd.com or contact them via email at pderosa.@cleanweb.com

Visit space centers: NASA John F. Kennedy Space Center and NASA Lyndon B. Johnson Space Center (other space centers are in various states; check your phone book, Chamber of Commerce for the state in which you live or library.)

Star labs: These are portable planetariums. There are several around the country and at some local schools.

Astronomical Society: Talk to local Astronomical society and find out when they star gaze, they often allow people to come out and watch!

University or College Campus: Many offer astronomy classes with times to view high-power telescopes open to the public

Space Camp: These programs are in Florida and Alabama; write or call for more information! U.S. Space Camp and U.S. Space Academy Alabama Space and Rocket Center, One Tranquillity Base Huntsville, AL 35807 1-800-633-7280

Star Finder Chart

Υ *Search the sky and list all the stars and constellations you can find. Keep a record of their position in the sky and date. Use a star finder or book to help.*

Gospel Message
in the Stars
Constellation
Star Charts

The following pages contain the original forty-eight constellations and their names. The stars are labeled to help you find them easily in the night sky. The accompanying drawing will help you "picture" the original meanings of the words as they were meant to be in the telling of the Gospel message. We hope you enjoy finding the Gospel message in the stars...

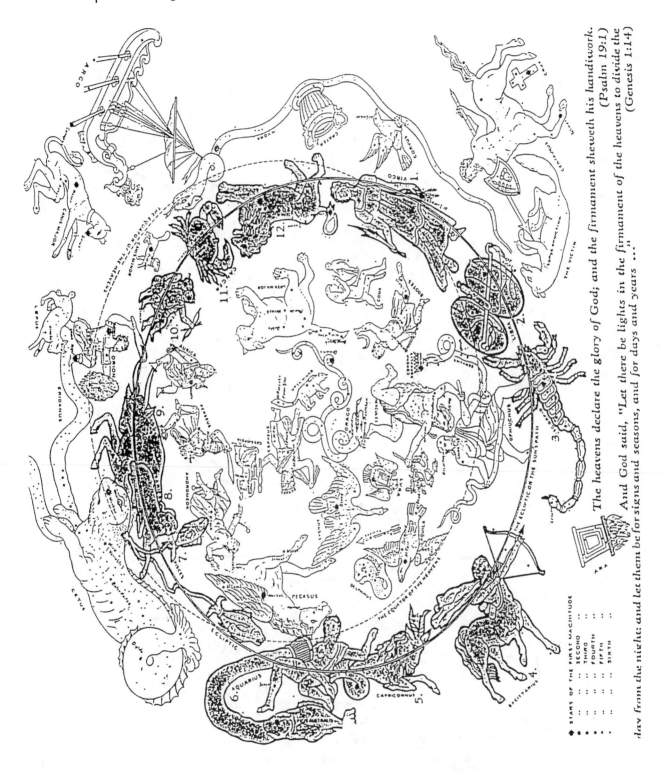

The heavens declare the glory of God; and the firmament sheweth his handiwork.
(Psalm 19:1)

And God said, "Let there be lights in the firmament of the heavens to divide the day from the night: and let them be for signs and seasons, and for days and years . . ."
(Genesis 1:14)

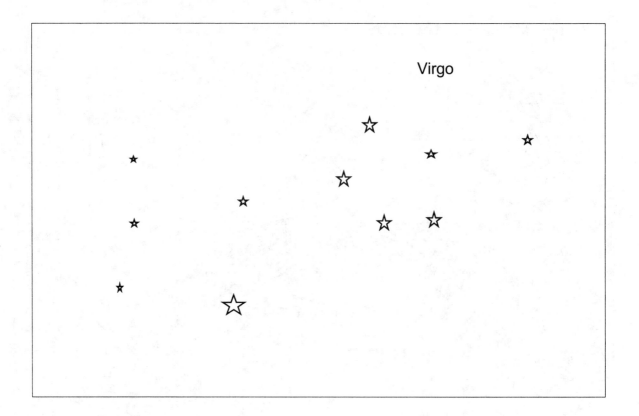

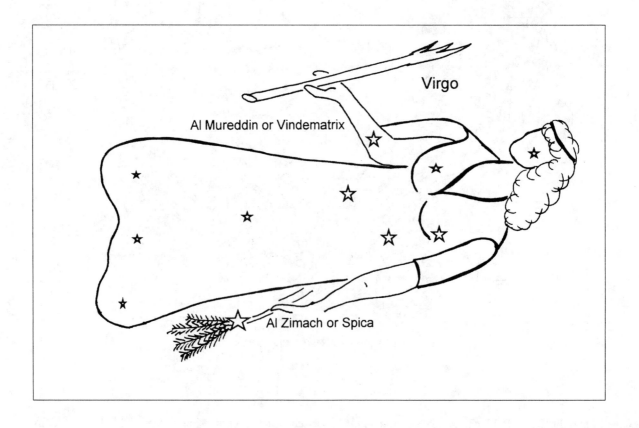

Coma

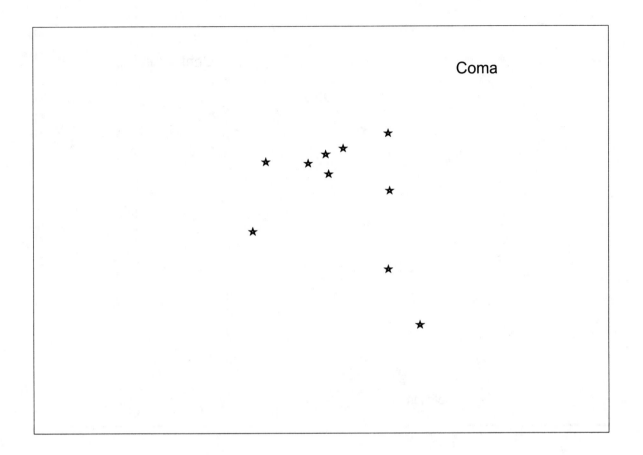

Coma

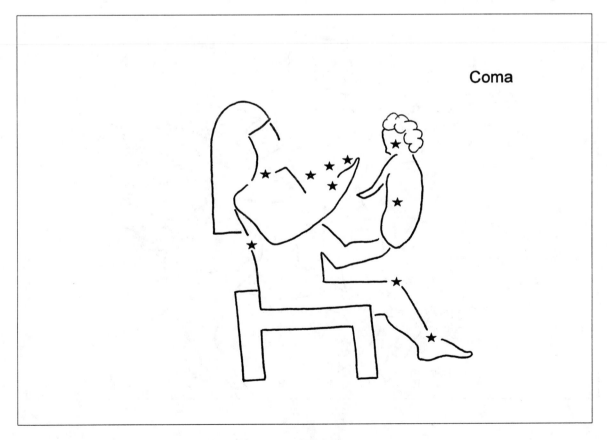

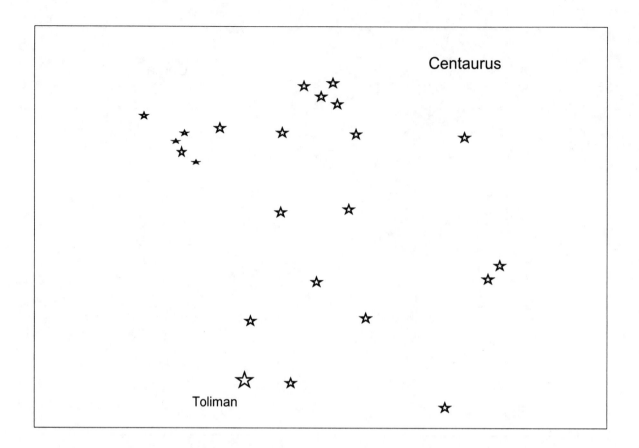

Centaurus

Toliman

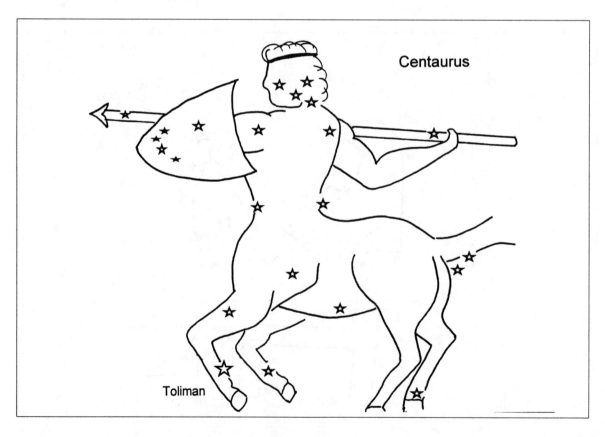

Centaurus

Toliman

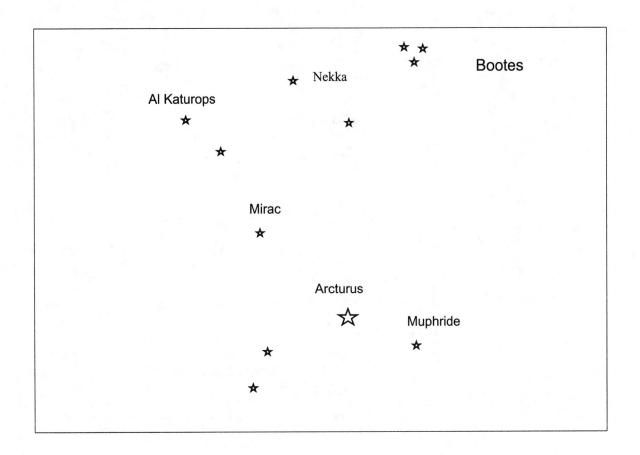

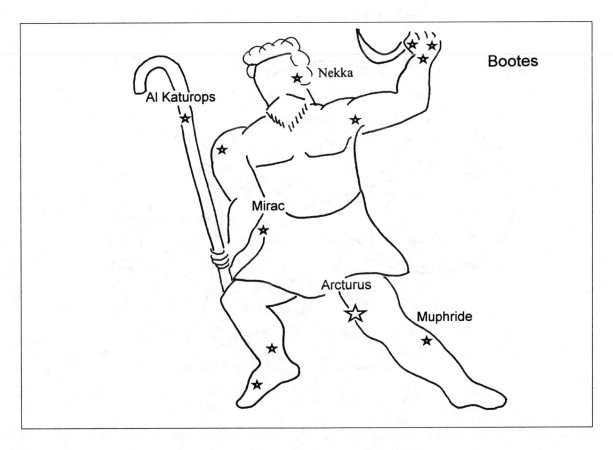

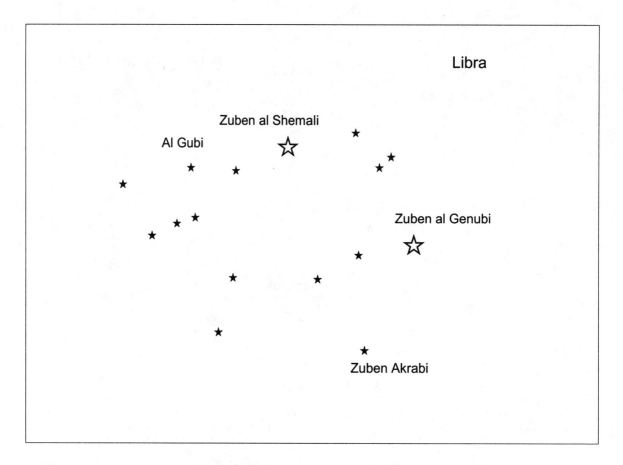

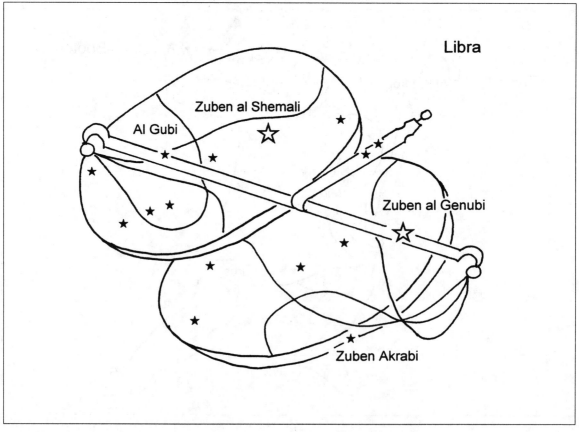

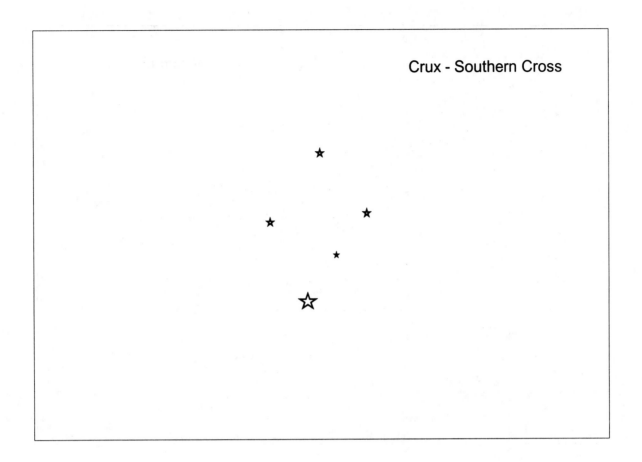

Crux - Southern Cross

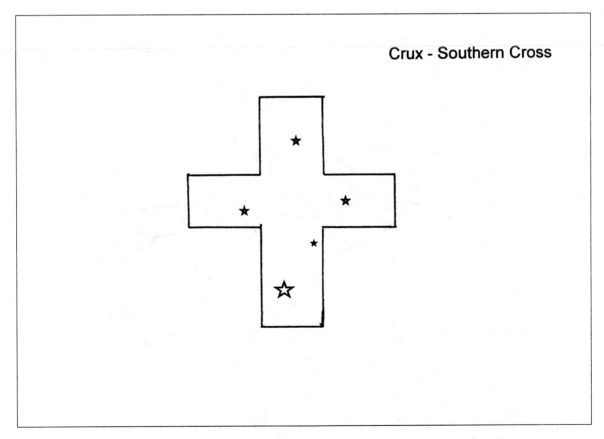

Crux - Southern Cross

125

Victima

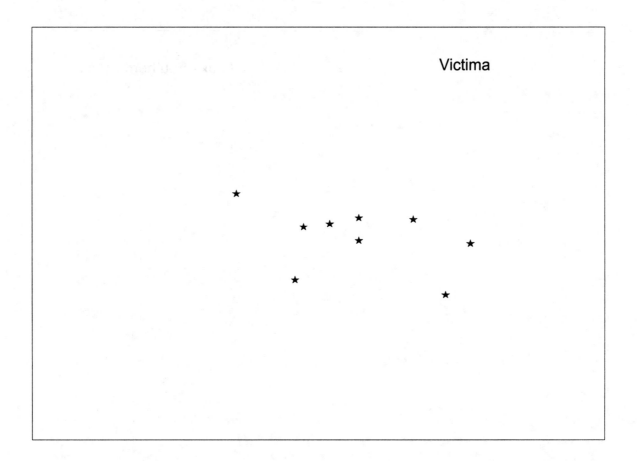

Victima

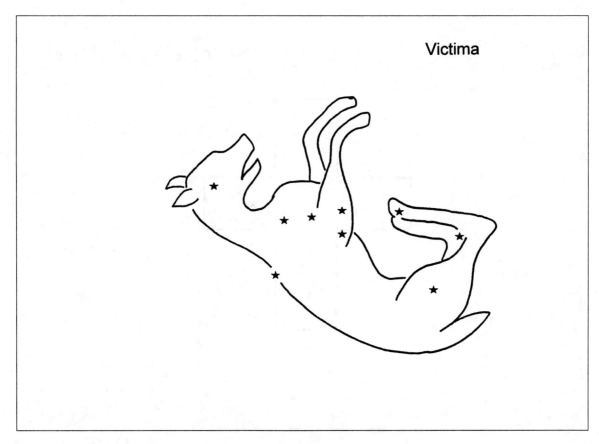

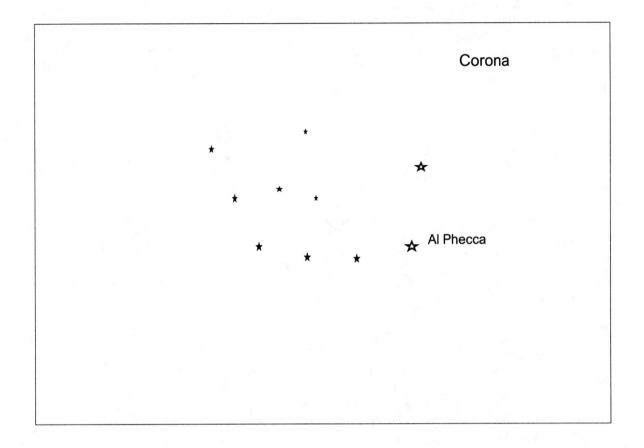

Corona

Al Phecca

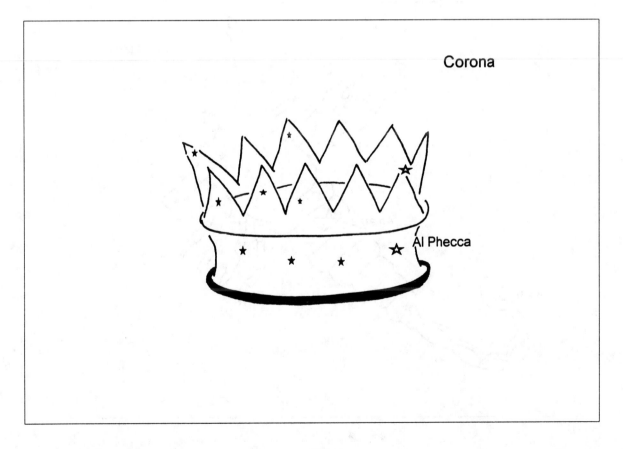

Corona

Al Phecca

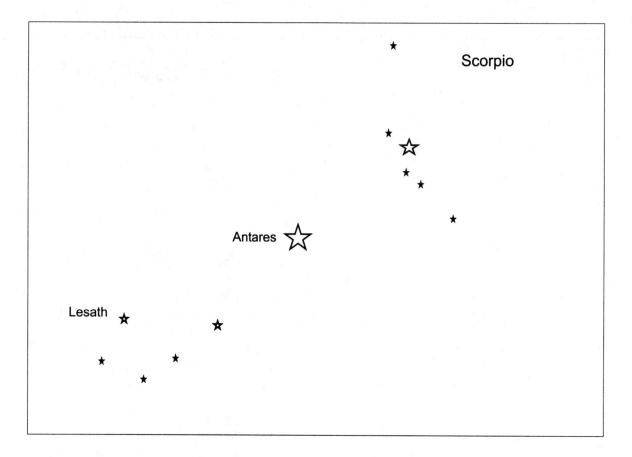

Scorpio

Antares

Lesath

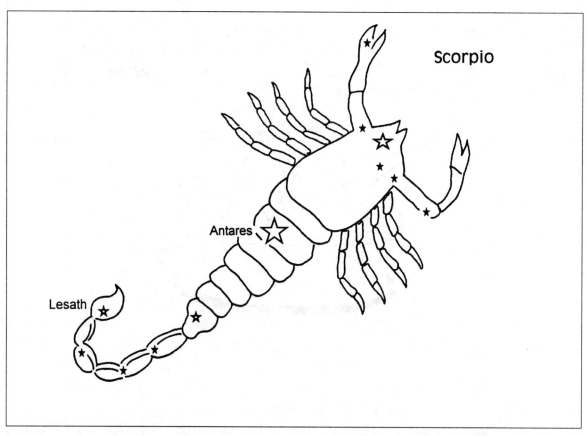

Scorpio

Antares

Lesath

128

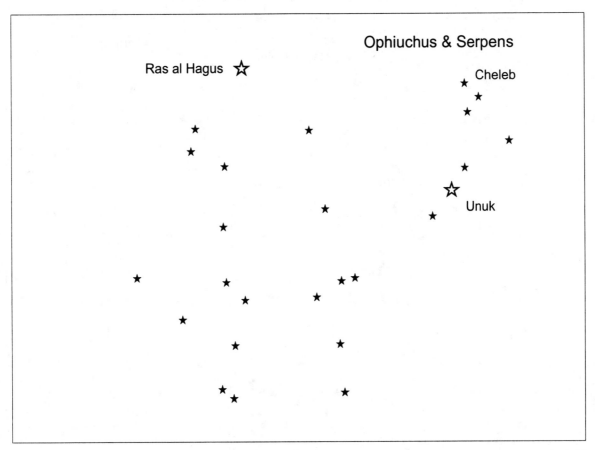

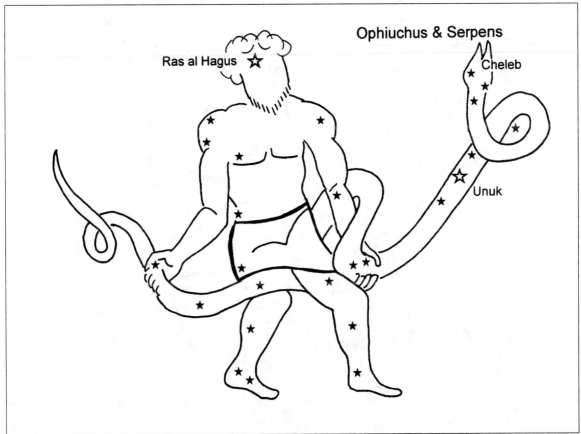

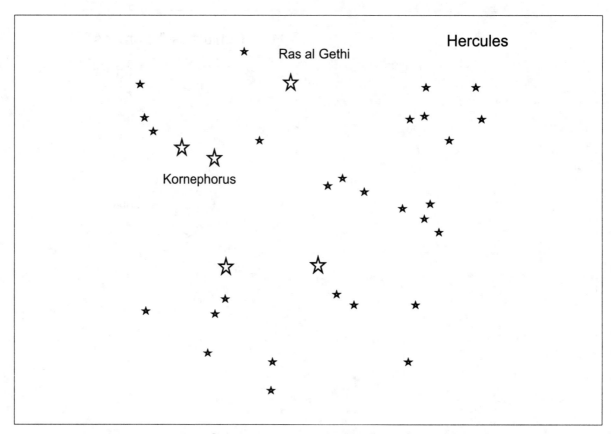

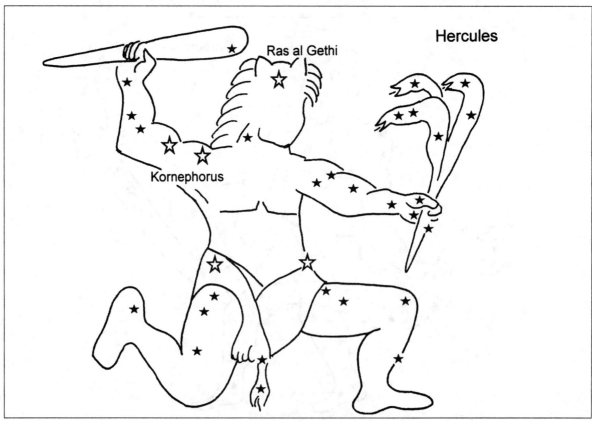

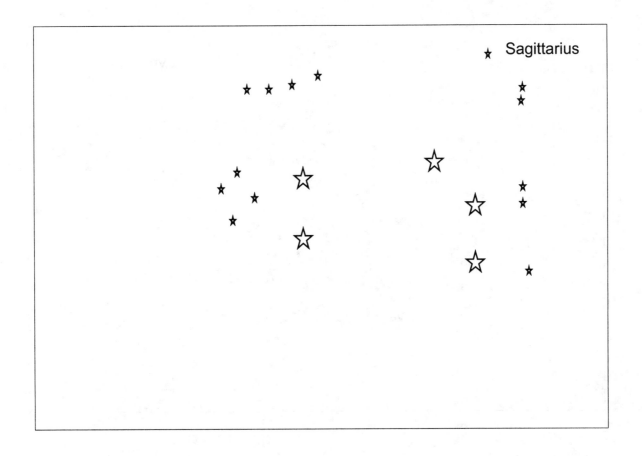

Sagittarius

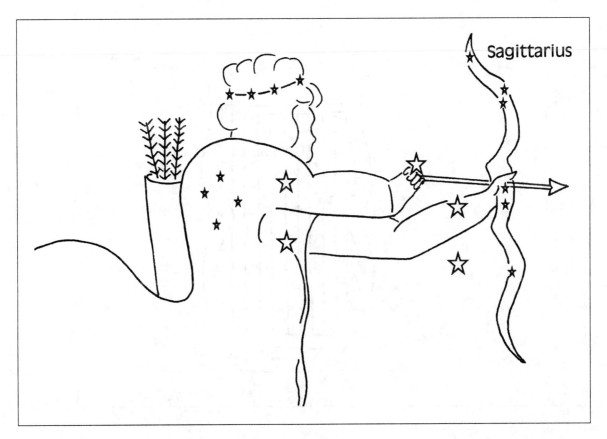

Sagittarius

131

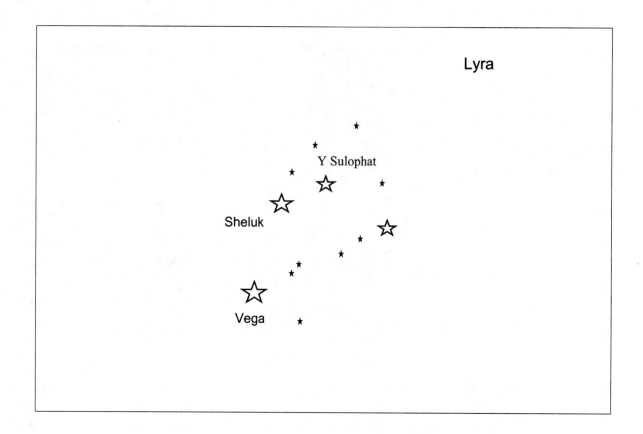

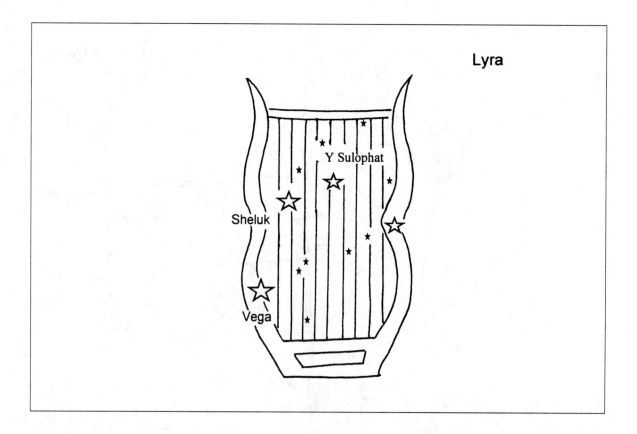

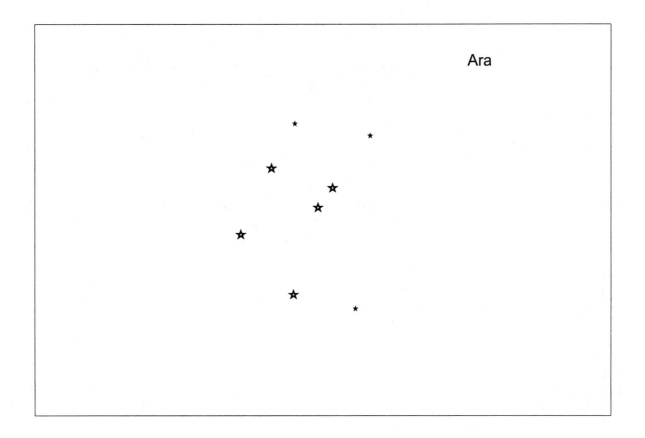

Ara

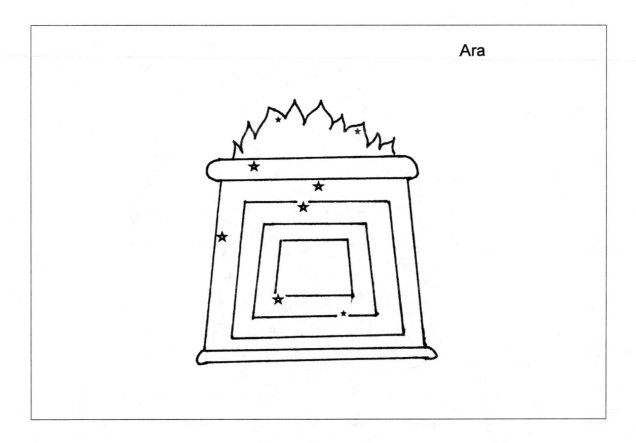

Ara

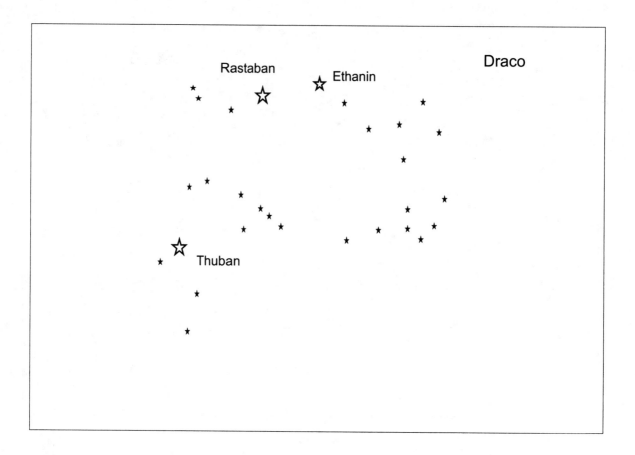

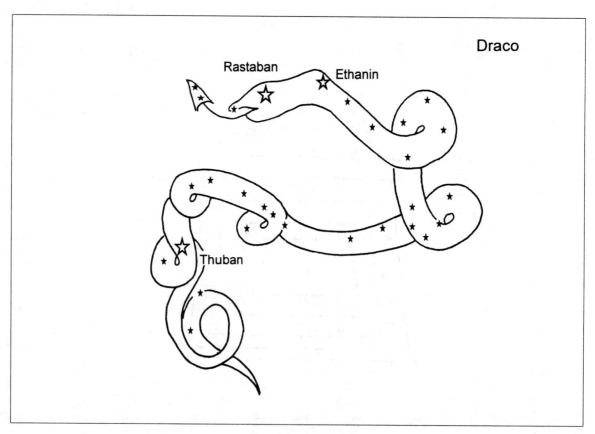

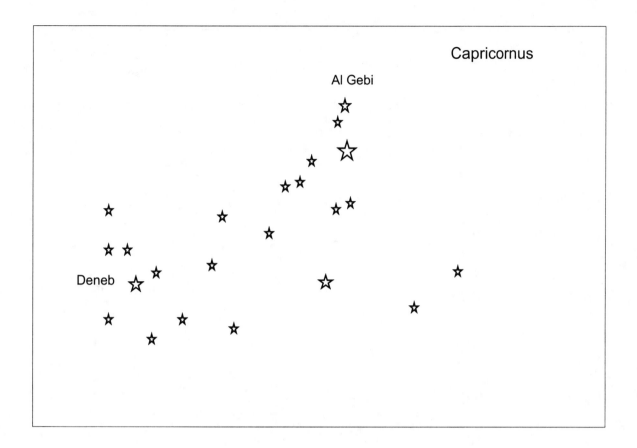

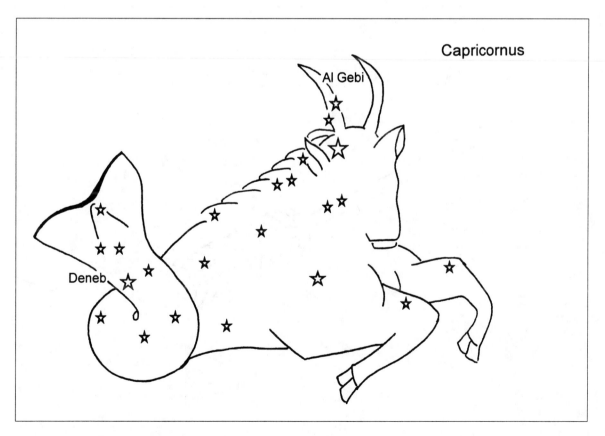

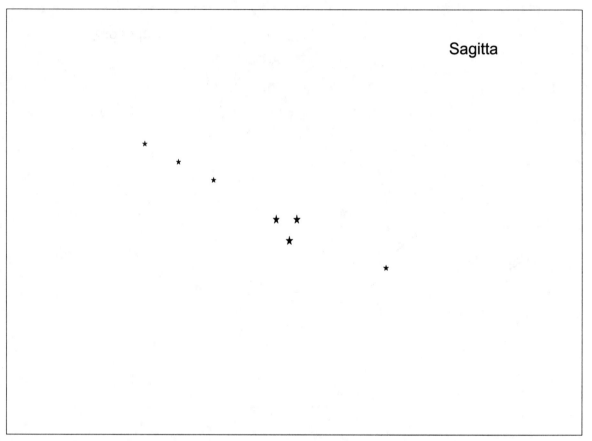

Sagitta

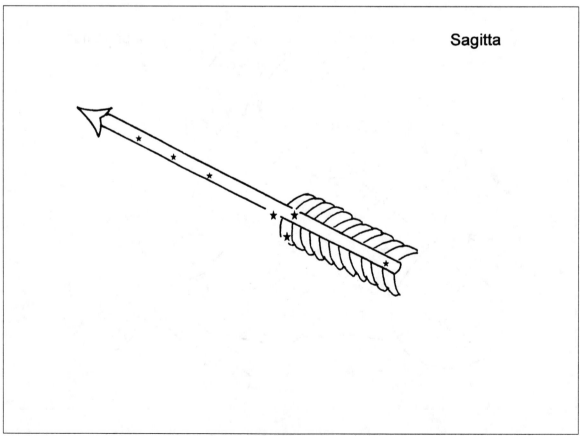

Sagitta

136

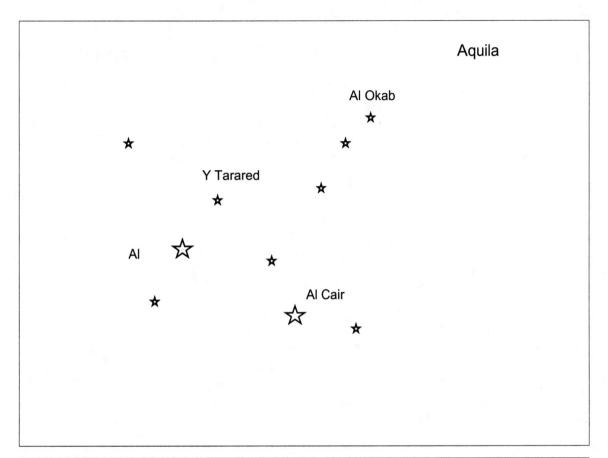

Aquila

Al Okab

Y Tarared

Al

Al Cair

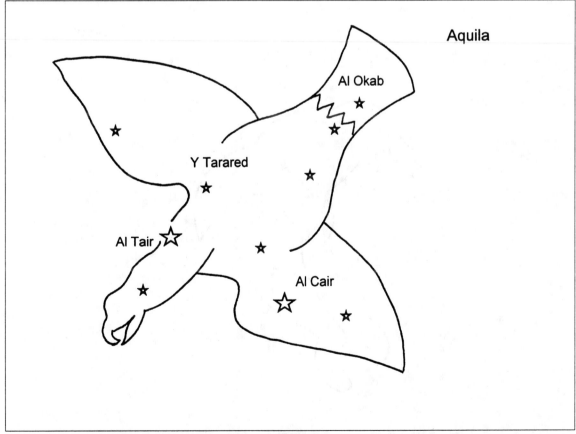

Aquila

Al Okab

Y Tarared

Al Tair

Al Cair

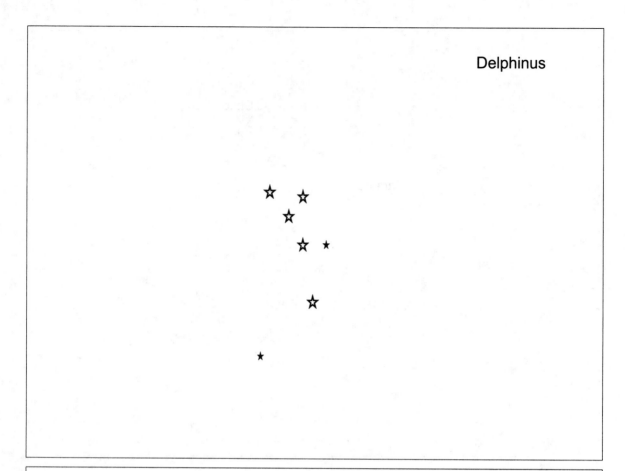

Delphinus

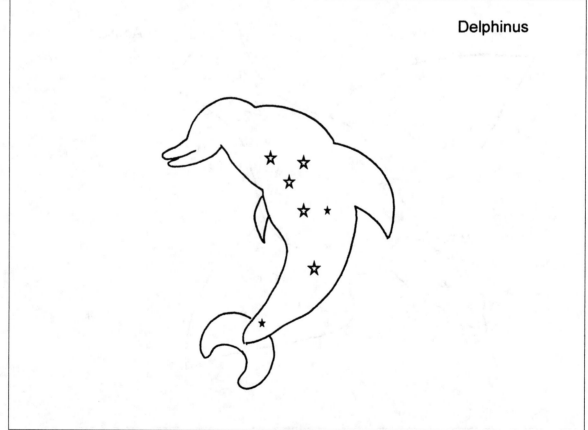

Delphinus

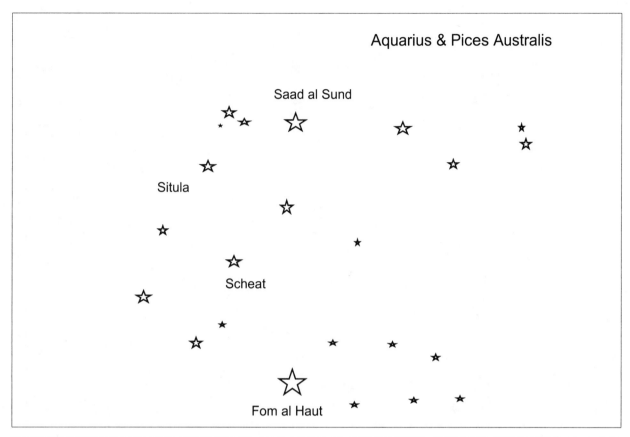

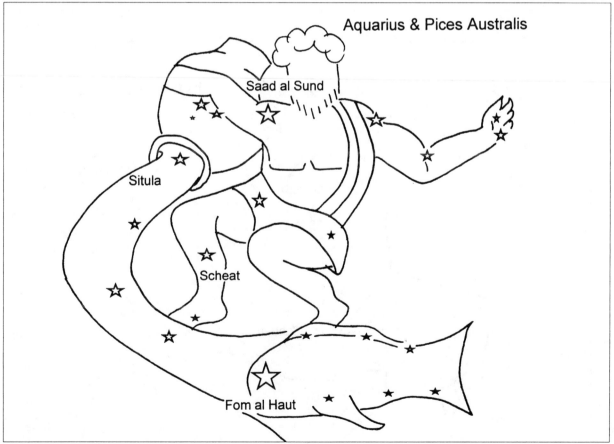

139

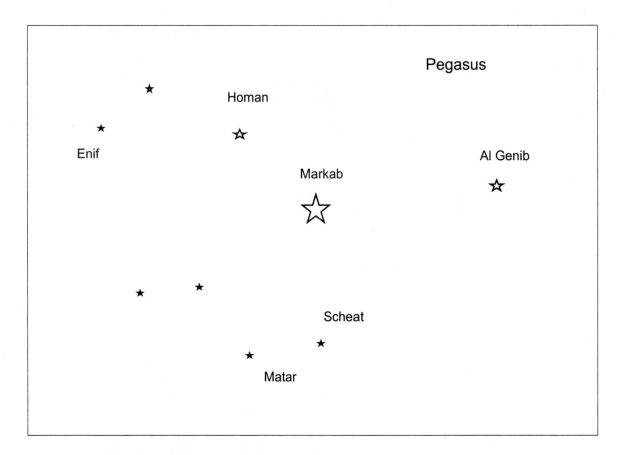

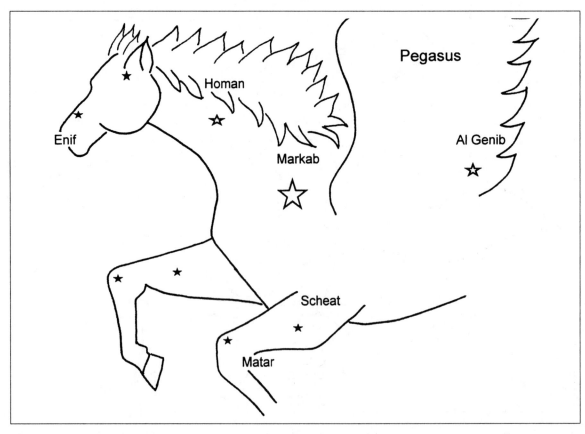

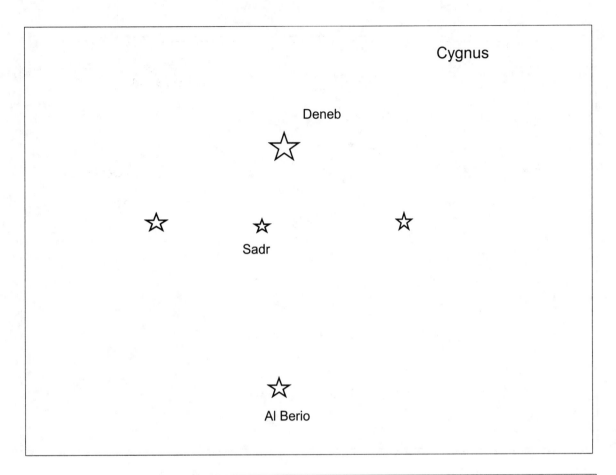

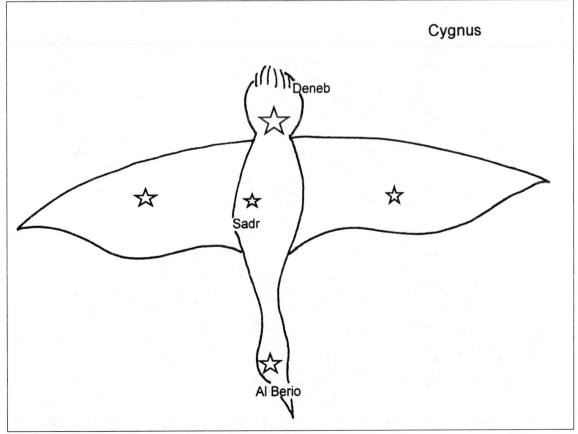

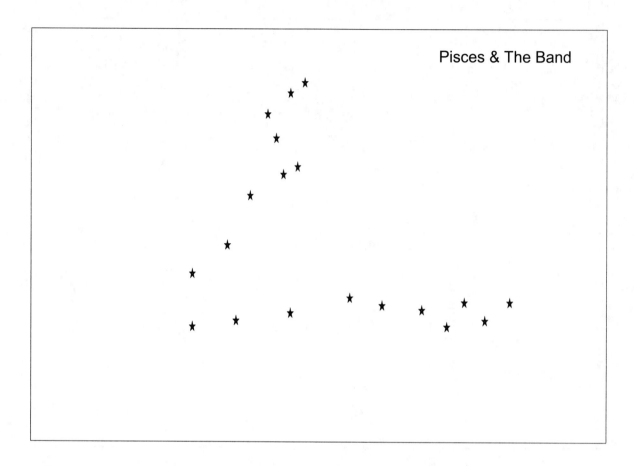

Pisces & The Band

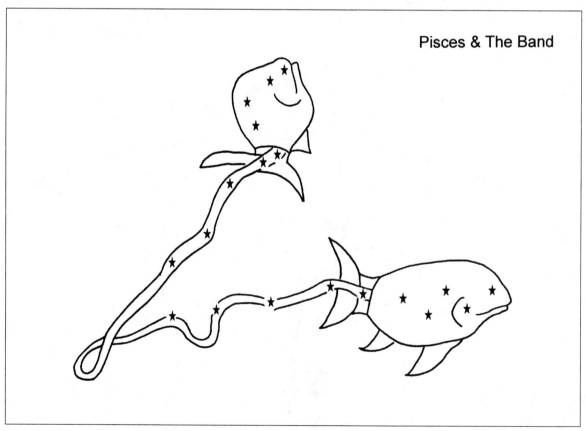

Pisces & The Band

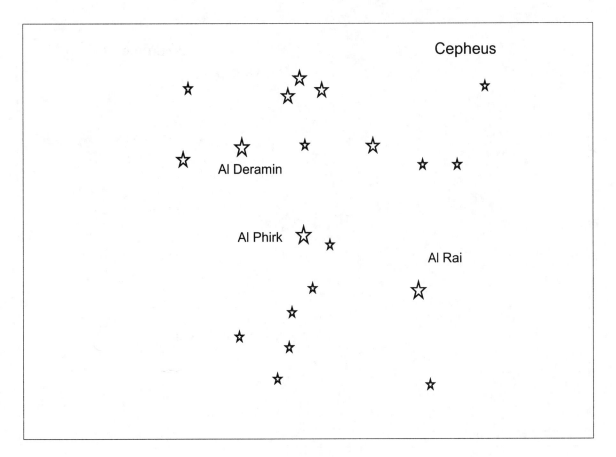

Cepheus

Al Deramin

Al Phirk

Al Rai

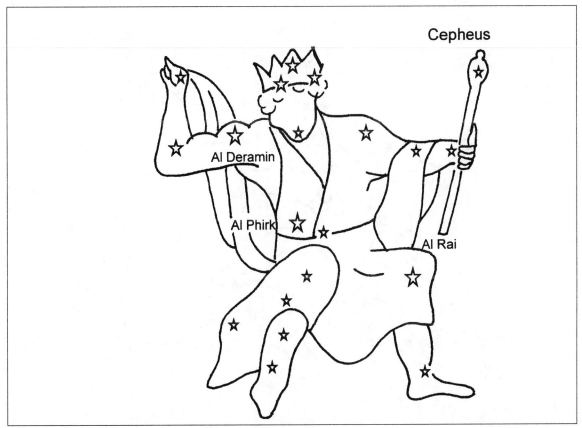

Cepheus

Al Deramin

Al Phirk

Al Rai

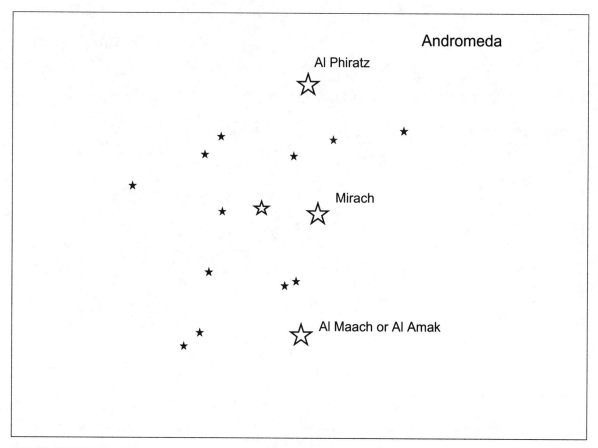

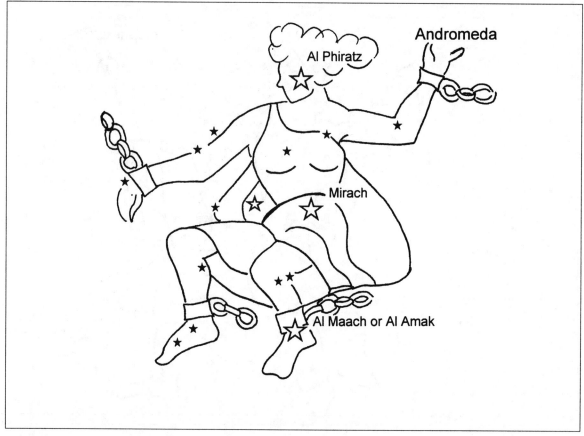

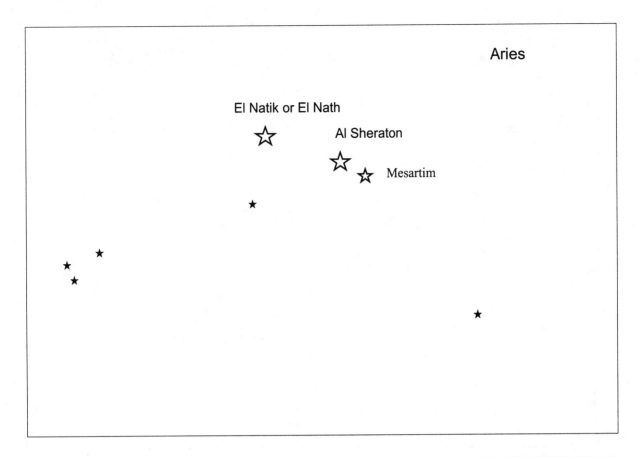

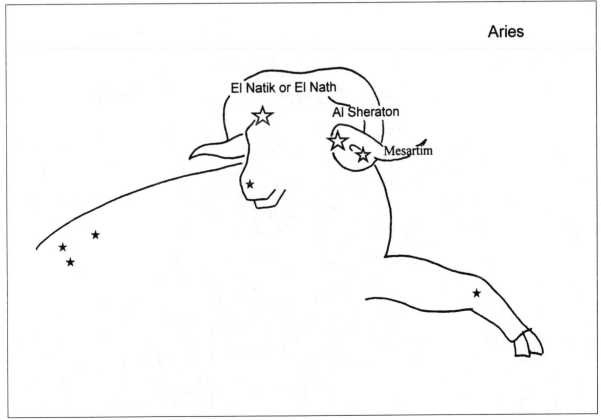

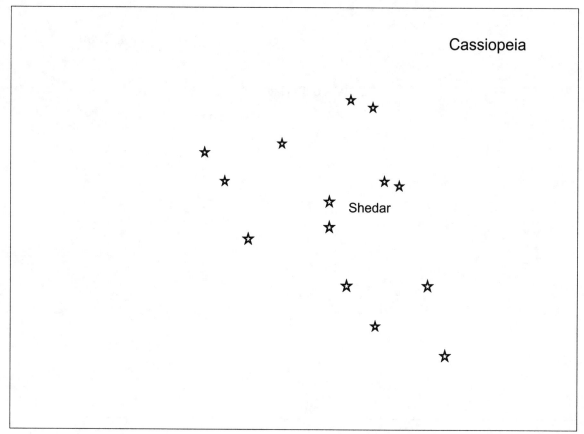

Cassiopeia

Shedar

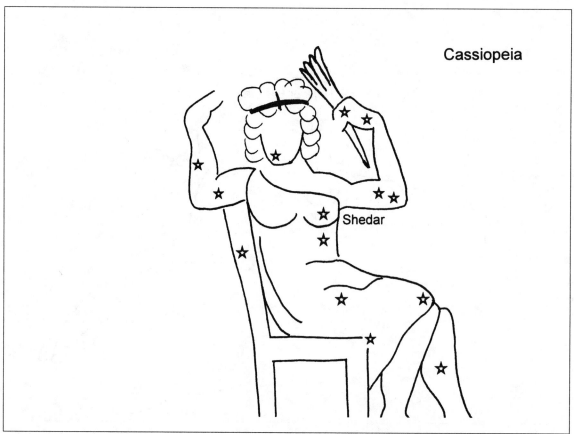

Cassiopeia

Shedar

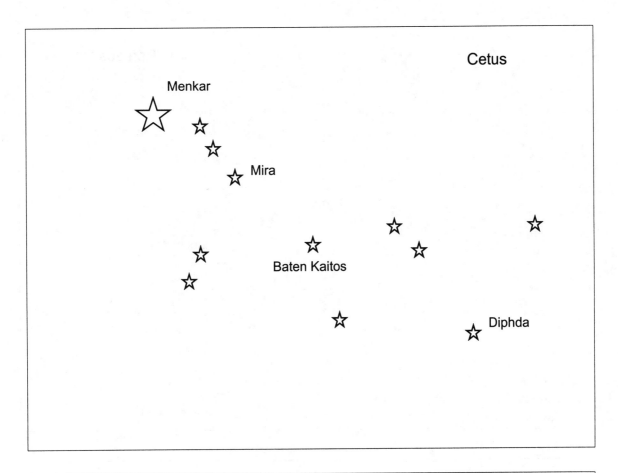

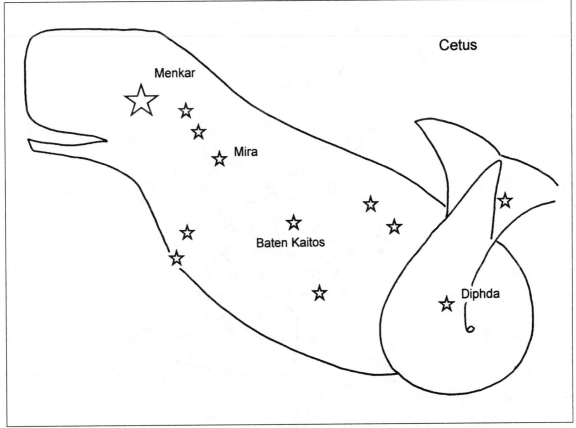

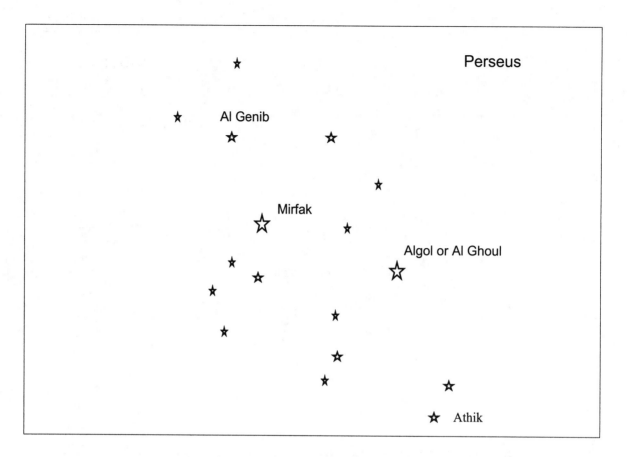

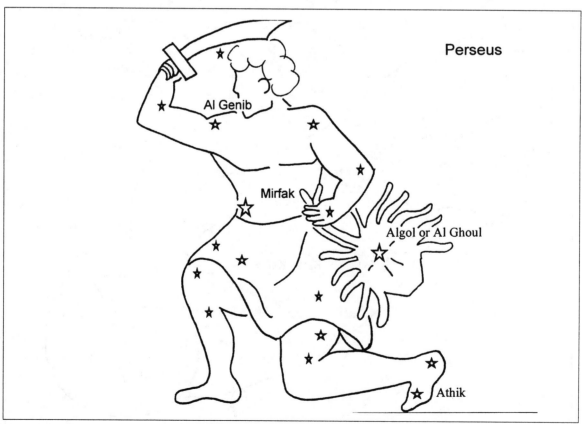

148

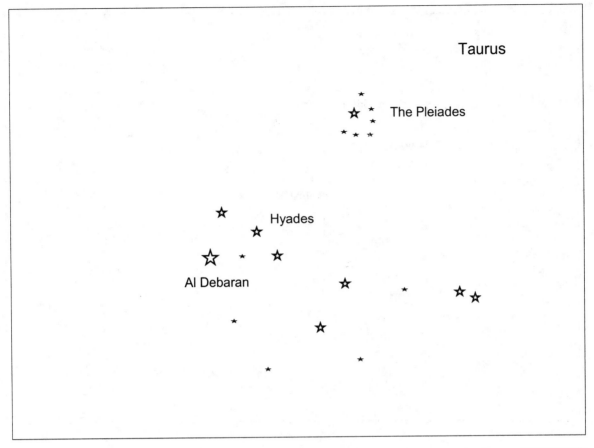

Taurus

The Pleiades

Hyades

Al Debaran

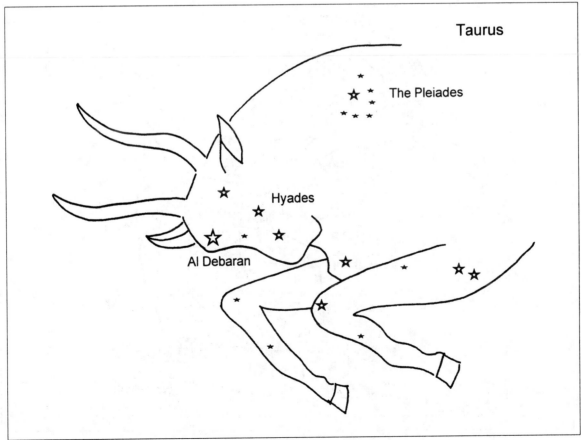

Taurus

The Pleiades

Hyades

Al Debaran

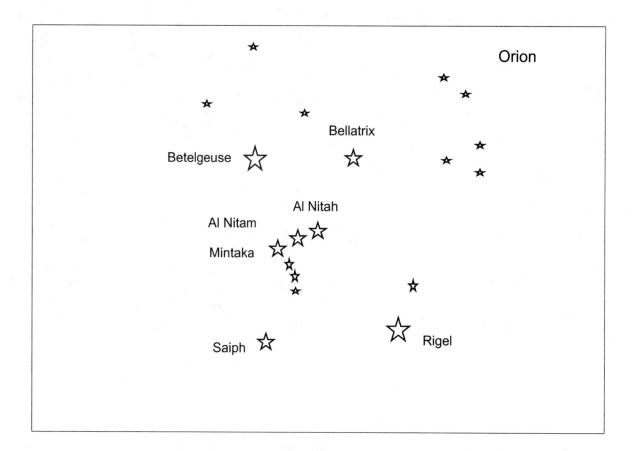

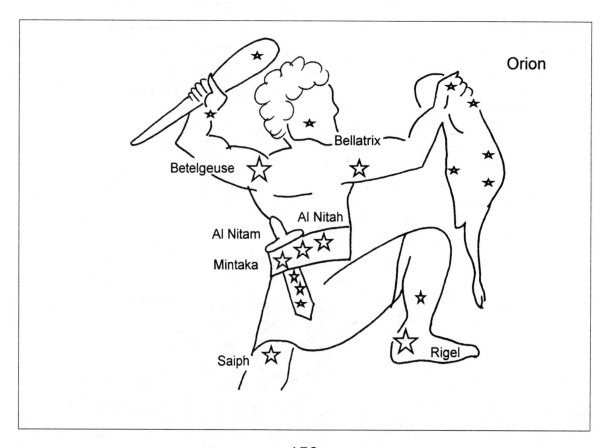

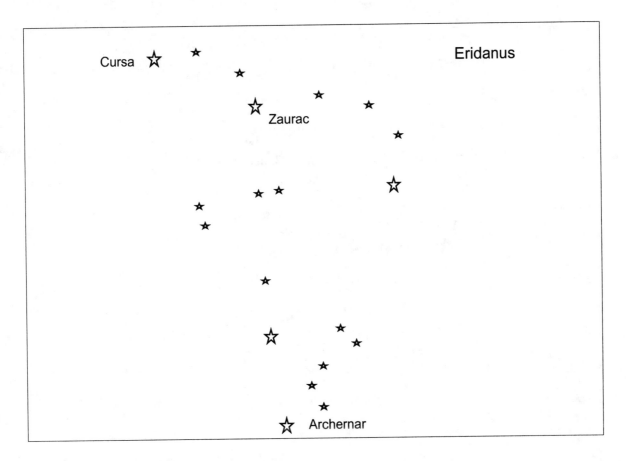

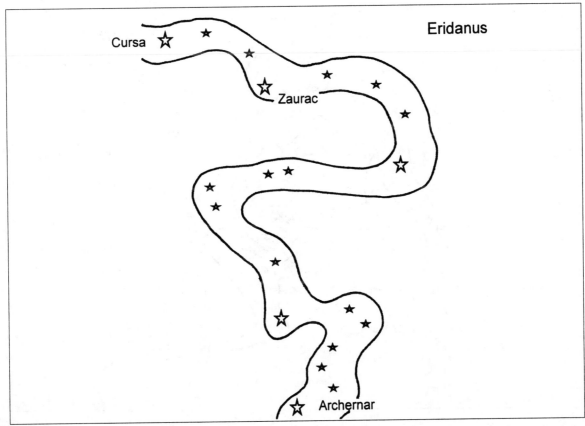

151

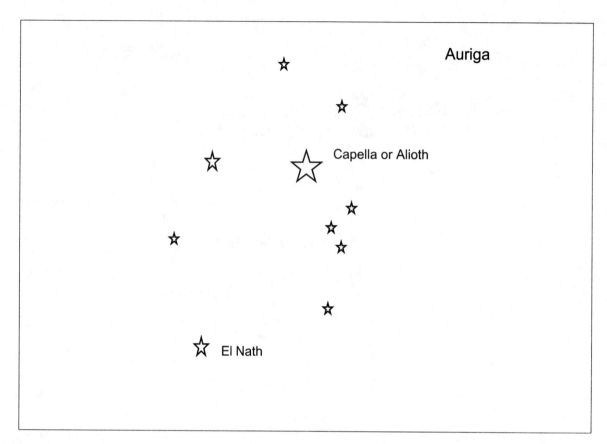

Auriga

Capella or Alioth

El Nath

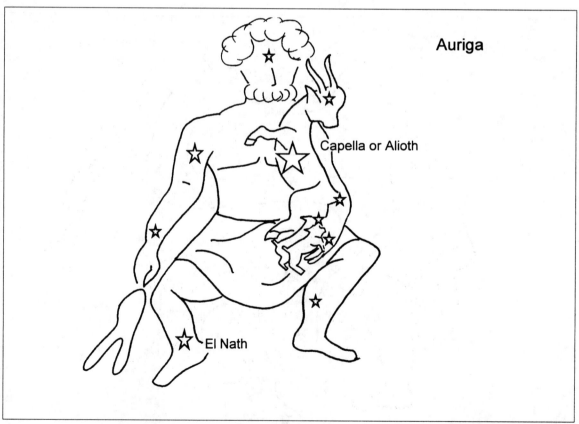

Auriga

Capella or Alioth

El Nath

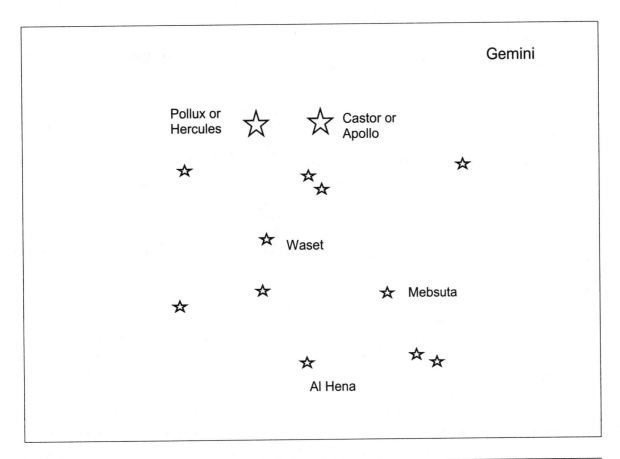

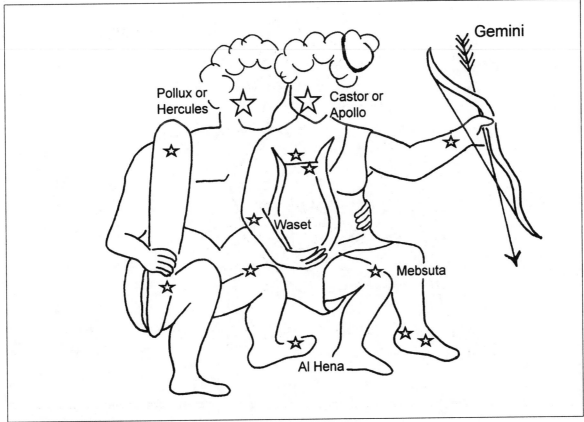

153

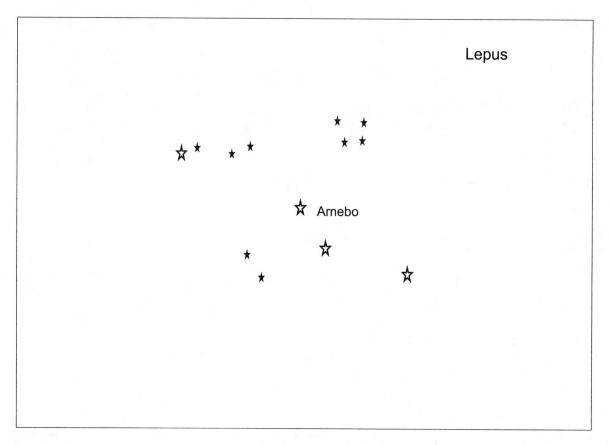

Lepus

Arnebo

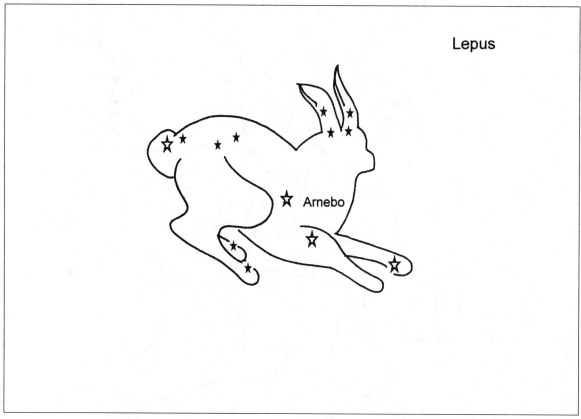

Lepus

Arnebo

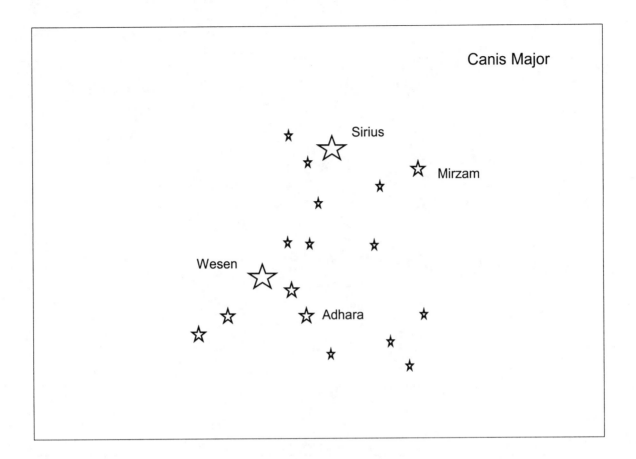

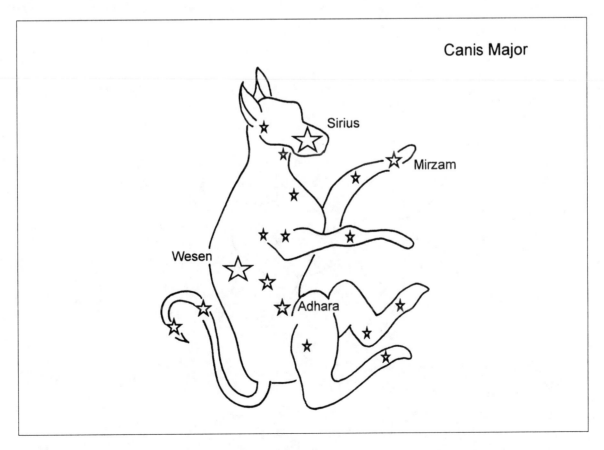

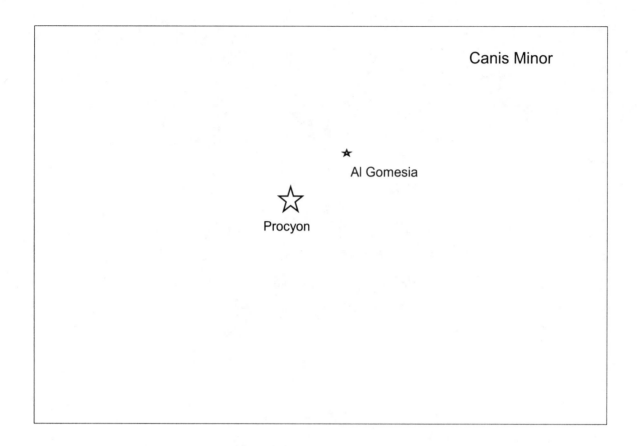

Canis Minor

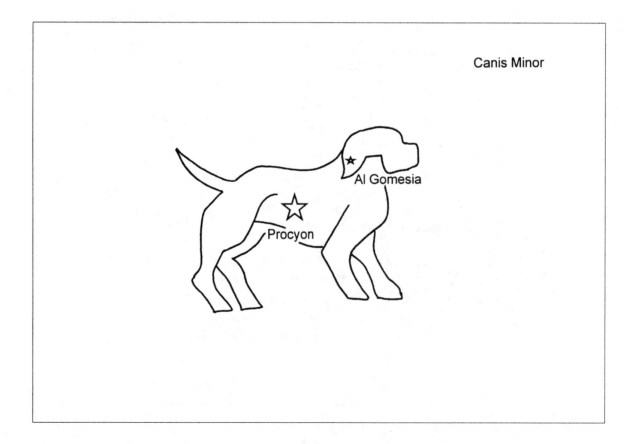

Canis Minor

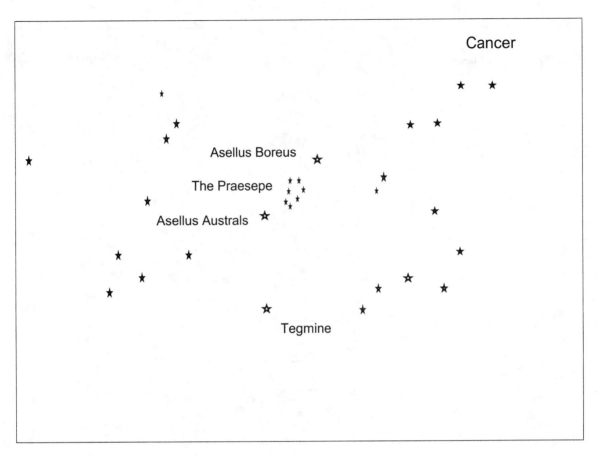

Cancer

Asellus Boreus

The Praesepe

Asellus Australs

Tegmine

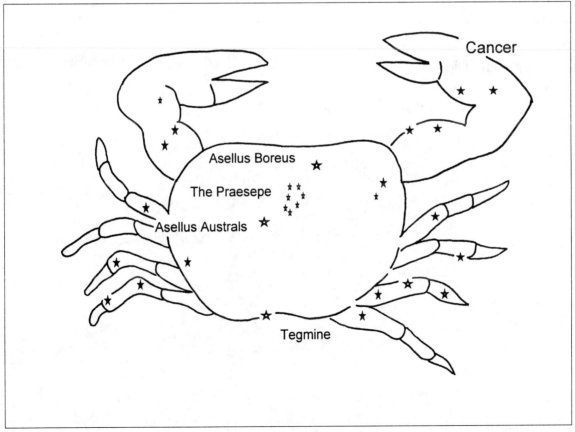

Cancer

Asellus Boreus

The Praesepe

Asellus Australs

Tegmine

157

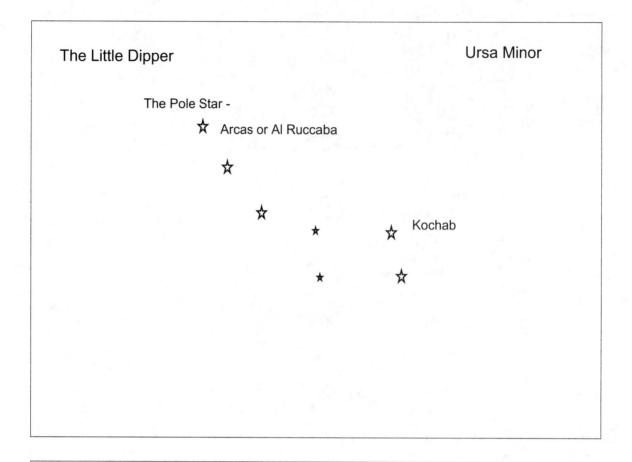

The Little Dipper

Ursa Minor

The Pole Star -

Arcas or Al Ruccaba

Kochab

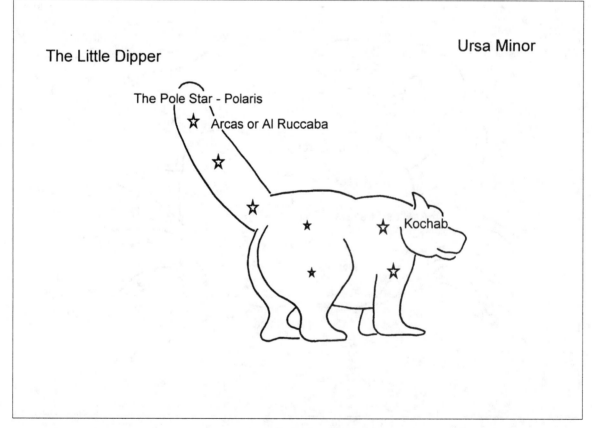

The Little Dipper

Ursa Minor

The Pole Star - Polaris

Arcas or Al Ruccaba

Kochab

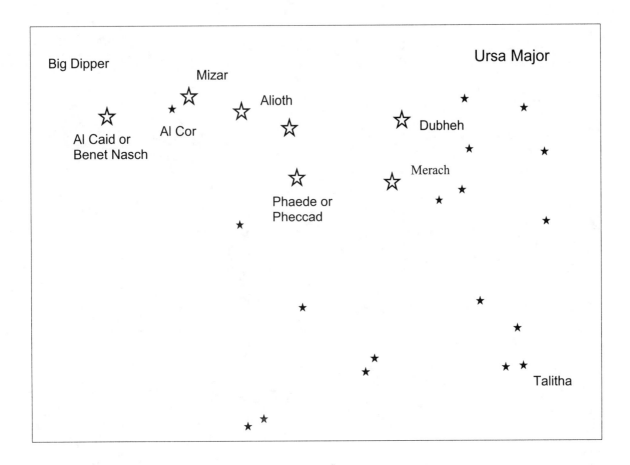

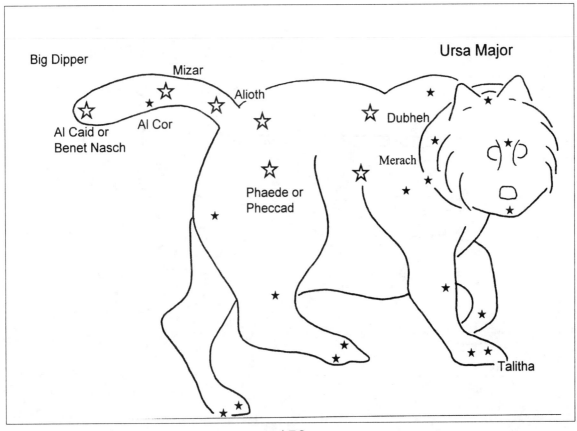

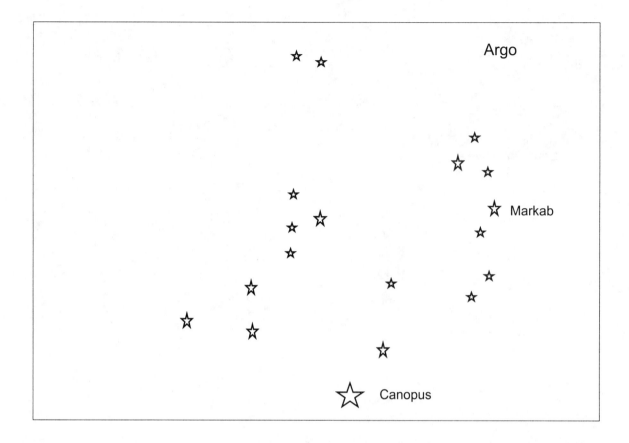

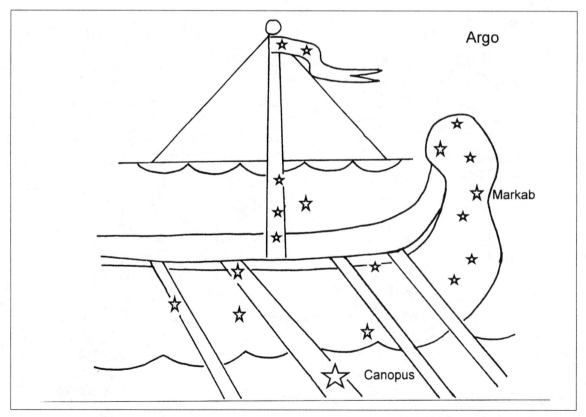

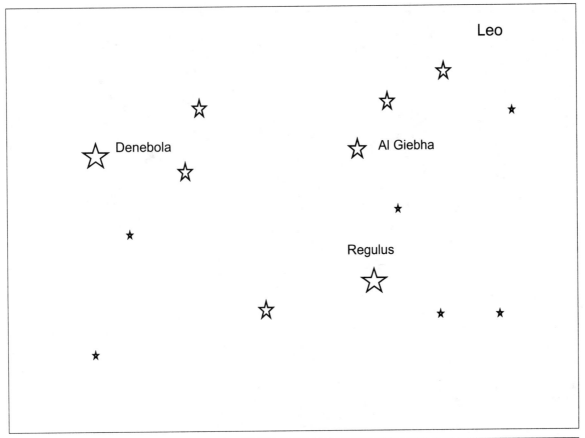

Leo

Denebola

Al Giebha

Regulus

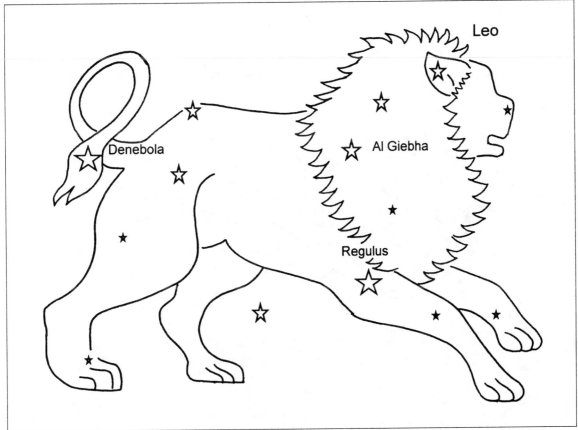

Leo

Denebola

Al Giebha

Regulus

161

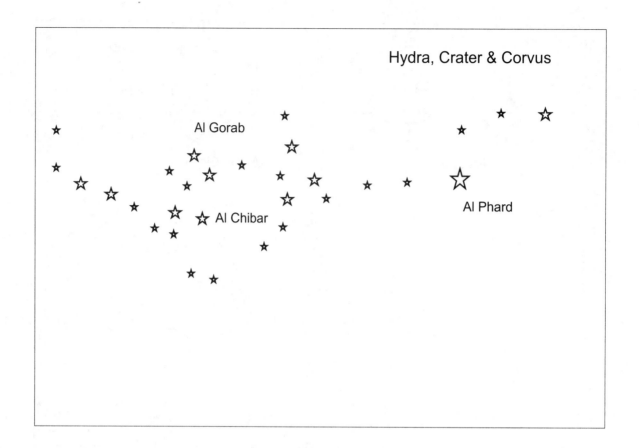

Hydra, Crater & Corvus

Al Gorab

Al Chibar

Al Phard

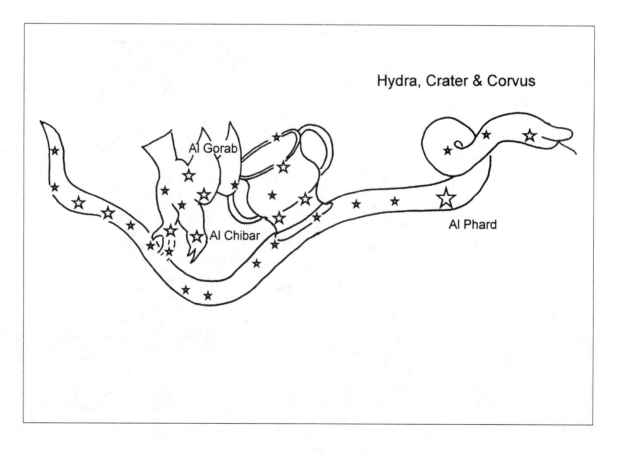

Hydra, Crater & Corvus

Al Gorab

Al Chibar

Al Phard

Science Experiment Planning Guide

SELECT THE TOPIC YOU WILL STUDY:

Remember to use the Science Keys!

1. Use the scientific method!
2. Use simple experiments that tie in with your overall unit.
3. Use experiments that require easy to find materials and ingredients.
4. Never say science is magic.
5. Make it simple and explain well!
6. Follow the experiment book like a recipe book-exactly!
7. Allow your children to DO the experiment themselves, with minimal help.
8. Allow your children to do variations of the experiment. Let them discover.
9. Allow your children to make a mess!
10. Be both flexible and scheduled.
11. Keep careful records.

The best way to teach science is to be prepared and to expect the unexpected.

Experiment!

Do I have all the supplies on hand I need?

CHECKLIST:
1. Did I plan **science** for this week?
2. Did I plan **experiments** for this week?
3. Do I have all the **materials** I need for the experiments?
4. Do these experiments tie into the overall **unit of study,** or **topic** we are studying?

1. Do I do the experiment more than one time? (Especially if the results do not meet my expectations.)
2. Do I use **resources** in researching my question?
3. Did I (or my child) **read information** pertaining to the topic we will be experimenting on?
4. Did I **explain** to my child why we are doing the experiment?
5. Does my child **understand** why we are doing the experiment?
6. Do we have enough **time** to do the experiment?

Experiment Planning Guide

Experiment: _____

_____

_____

Days needed to complete: _____

Books needed: _____

_____

_____

_____

Materials Needed: _____

_____

_____

_____

_____

_____

_____

_____

_____

_____

_____

SCIENCE EXPERIMENT

Question: (What is the experiment about?)

My Guess: (What I think will happen.)

Materials: (What I used.)

What did I do?

What Happened? **BEFORE PICTURE**	What Happened? **AFTER PICTURE**

Why did it happen?

Science Experiment

TITLE OF MY EXPERIMENT

_____

Question: (What is the experiment about?)

My Guess: (What I think will happen?)

Materials: (What I used)

What I did:

What happened?

Why did it happen?

SCIENCE EXPERIMENT

TITLE OF MY EXPERIMENT

Question: (What is the experiment about?)

My Guess: (What I think will happen.)

Materials: (What I used.)

Procedure (What I did.)

Observation (What happened?)

Conclusion (Why did it happen?)

SCIENCE EXPERIMENT

Question:

Hypothesis:

Materials:

Procedure:

Observation/Data:

Conclusion:

References

Ackerman, Paul D., 1993. *It's A Young World After All.* Grand Rapids, Mi; Baker Books.

Akridge, Russell. *The Sun is Shrinking.* Impact Article No. 82, Institute of Creation Research

Bliss, Richard. 1991. *Voyage to the Stars.* El Cajon, CA Institute for Creation Research.

Brown, Walter T. 1989. *In The Beginning...* Phoenix, AZ: Center for Scientific Creation.

Clark, Robert T. and James D. Bales. 1966. *Why Scientists Accept Evolution.* Grand Rapids, MI: Baker Book House.

DeYoung, Donald. 1994. *Science and the Bible.* Grand Rapids, MI: Baker Books.

Flamsteed, Sam. 1995. "Cosmography—Crisis in theCosmos." *Discover Magazine.* 16, no. 3, p. 66.

Freedman, Wendy, L. 1992. "The Expansion Rate and Size of the Universe." *Scientific American.* November. 267 no. 5., p. 54.

Gerwitz, Felice and Jill Whitlock. 1997. *Creation Science A Study Guide to Creation!* rev. ed. Ft. Myers, FL: Media Angels.

Griffiths, Richard. 1995. "The Faint Blue Yonder." *Discover Magazine.* 16, No.11.

Hatchett, Clint. 1988. *The Glow- In-The-Dark Night Sky Book.* New York, NY: Random House.

Humphryes, Russell. 1995. *Starlight and TIme: Solving the Puzzle of Distant Starlight in a Young Universe.* Colorado Springs, CO: Master Books.

Jones, Brian and Stephen Edberg, Ed., *The Practical Astronomer.* New York, NY: Simon and Schuster.

Lemonick, Michael D., and Madeline Nash. 1995. "Unravelling Universe". *Time.* 6 March, 1995. p.76-84.

Maddox, John. 1989. Editorial "Down with the Big Bang," *Nature.* 10 August.

Mallove, Eugene F., 2002. "The Implications of the 'Big Bang.'" *Infinite Energy.* 46, no. 8, p. 7.

McMurtry, Grady. Speaker. 1994. *Creation Science Seminar.* Bonita Springs, Florida.

Morris, Henry M. 1974. *Many Infallible Proofs.* El Cajon, CA: Master Books.

Morris, Henry M. 1985. *Scientific Creationism.* El Cajon, CA: Master Books.

Morris, Henry M. 1989. *Science, Scripture, and The Young Earth.* El Cajon, CA: Institute for Creation Research.

Mulfinger, George Jr. 1983. *Design and Origins in Astronomy.* Terre Haute, IN: Creation Research Society Books.

Petersen, Dennis R. 1990. *Unlocking the Mysteries of Creation.* El Dorado, CA: Creation Resource Foundation.

Peterson, Dennis R. 2002. *Unlocking the Mysteries of Creation.* El Dorado, CA: Master Books. Public Broadcasting System. 1994 - On the 25th Anniversary of the First Moon Walk.

Rey, H. A. 1988. *Find the Constellations.* Boston, MA: Houghton Mifflin Company.

Seiss, Joseph A., [1882] 1972. *The Gospel In The Stars.* Grand Rapids, MI: Kregel Publications.

Setterfield, Barry. Year . "The Velocity of Light and the Age of the Universe" *Technical Monograph* from the Creation Science Foundation.

Slusher, Harold S., & Stephen J. Robertson. 1982. *The Age Of The Solar System - A study of the Poynting-Robertson Effect and extinction of interplanetary dust.* El Cajon, CA.: Institute for Creation Research.

Thompson, Bert. 1986. *The Scientific Case for Creation.* Montgomery, AL: Apologetics Press, Inc.

Van Flandern, Tom., 2002. "The Top 30 Problems with the Big Bang." *Infinite Energy.* 46, no. 8, p. 10.

White, A.J. Monty. 1985. *How Old Is The Earth?* Welwyn, Herts, England:Evangelical Press.

Zim, Herbert S., and Robert H. Baker. 1975. *Stars.* New York, NY: Golden Press.

To order send check plus (6% tax FL residents only) and 15% shipping (US orders only) to Media Angels 16450 S Tamiami Trail, Suite 3, Ft. Myers, FL 33908

Teaching Science and Having Fun! by Felice Gerwitz. $12.95
        This handy teacher's reference includes how to schedule, what to teach, a scope and sequence, the scientific method, how to set up a lab, how to choose a microscope, resources and much more! Felice, a former classroom teacher, has homeschooled since 1986, holds science workshops for children, and conducts seminars for adults.

An Insider's Guide to Successful Science Fair Projects by Felice Gerwitz. $6.50
        A handy guide for helping parents and children put together a winning Science Fair Project! Great science fair strategies, how to plan, where to look for information, the scientific method, keeping a journal, writing a report and abstract, display guidelines, what judges look for and much more!

Virtual Field Trips: An Online Study Guide by Felice Gerwitz $18.95
        Take a virtual trip in the comfort of your own home. Fun field trips are mapped out for you with scavenger hunt questions to answer along the way. Or try the website www.Virtual-Field-Trips.com

Creation Science Unit Studies: by Felice Gerwitz and Jill Whitlock
        Each fantastic study guide is written from a Biblical Creationist perspective, on three levels spanning K-12 Includes a teaching outline, activities, experiments, activities, resources, reproducible sheets and much more!
        Creation Science: A Study Guide to Creation! $16.95
        Creation Geology: A Study Guide to Fossils, Formations and the Flood! $18.95
        Creation Anatomy: A Study Guide to the Miracles of the Body! $18.95
        Creation Astronomy: A Study Guide to the Constellations! $18.95
        Science Hands-On Experiment and Activity Pack by Gerwitz
            This pack contains ready-to-copy activities and experiments; includes directions and scientific method sheets, games and crossword puzzles, glossary and much more. This resource compliments the unit study guides. Geology and Creation Science, Astronomy or Anatomy: $12.95 ea.

Truth Seekers Mystery Series™ Join Christian and Anna Murphy as they face action, adventure, mystery, and heart-stopping suspense and learn the truth will set you free! Creation based adventure novels for the entire family: Current titles: The Missing Link: Found $7.99, Dinosaur Quest at Diamond Peak $7.99 Keys to the Past: Unlocked $8.99

Acknowledgments
        To Jim Kregel President of Kregel publications who graciously gave us permission to synopsize *The Gospel in the Stars* written by Joseph A. Seiss. Thank you!

About the Authors
        Felice Gerwitz is owner of Media Angels, Inc., along with her husband Jeff. Felice has home schooled since 1986. She has a degree in Elementary Education, Learning Disabilities, and Early Childhood Education. To contact Felice email her at MediaAngels@aol.com.

        As a child, Jill Whitlock loved to lie out under the stars looking at the constellations. In high school, she wanted to become the first woman astronaut and fly to the moon. After graduating from Texas A & M University, Jill worked as an exploration Geologist in Denver, Co. In December 1983, she accepted Jesus Christ as her Savior and began praying and studying about the Creation vs. evolution question. Jill was especially intrigued by the Scripture "The heavens declare the glory of God", and she renewed her interest in studying the stars which led her to the study of the Gospel message in the stars. She now holds Creation Science seminars for Churches and other groups, which includes the Gospel message in the stars. She has been homeschooling their boys since 1986. To contact Jill email her at Whitlock@Sprynet.com